MEASUREMENT

CONTENTS

This edition published 1991 by
Franklin Watts
96 Leonard Street
London EC2A 4RH

ISBN 0 7496 0656 8

Printed in Belgium

Original edition published 1990 by
Hobsons Publishing plc
Sponsored by the National Physical
Laboratory

A CIP catalogue record for this book is
available from the British Library

Acknowledgements
We are grateful to the National Physical Laboratory for their help in the preparation of this publication, particularly to Dr Ian Leigh, Julia Johnson and Eileen Doran, and to the following individuals and organizations for providing photographic and illustrative material: BOC Group, Dr Tony Brain, Dr Jeremy Burgess, Ciba-Geigy, CNRI, Dynamic Imaging, English Heritage Library, ESA, Malcolm Fielding, David Gifford, GKN, Ralph Hutchings, Jaguar, John Laing, Michael Le Poer Trench, Tim Malyon, Martin Marietta Aerospace, National Motor Museum, National Physical Laboratory, National Westminster Bank, Mark Shearman, Mary Evans Picture Library, Meteorological Office, David Parker, Rolls Royce, Royal Greenwich Observatory, Rev Ronald Royer, Science Photo Library, Scottish Hydroelectric, Scottish Tourist Board, Shell Photo Service, Sinclair Stammers, Smiths Industries, State University of New York, Times Newspapers, US Naval Observatory, K Woodley.

MEASUREMENT

Keith Bridgeman

FRANKLIN WATTS
LONDON • NEW YORK • SYDNEY • TORONTO

1: WHY MEASURE?

Measurement is something we take for granted. Almost everything we do is measured. Measurement is necessary in order to achieve fair play and to keep us comfortable, healthy and entertained. When records in sports are broken the newspapers tell us with banner headlines. Measurement must therefore be important.

In this book we shall be looking at some of the measurements scientists make and how they affect the way we live.

All measurement is simply a comparison. We compare the thing we want to measure with something else which has already been measured (or calibrated). In order to calibrate different things we need standard measurements with which everybody agrees. The National Physical Laboratory is the focus of the UK's National Measurement System and keeps the standards of physical quantities which have been agreed internationally. By using these standards we can all make the same scientific comparisons.

What to measure?

When athletes compete in the 100 m sprint in the Olympic Games it is the first runner over the finishing line who wins. The time taken to run the race is also important. By comparing the time that winners of different races take to run the same distance we can then see which of the winners is the best. Ultimately we can compare races that are run several years apart and we can find out which athlete is fastest in the world. For this to work the same standards of time and distance measurement must be used in every race.

Similarly, standards apply when we buy a car. An advertisement might say '0-60 miles per hour in 7 seconds and able to travel 38 miles per gallon'. These measurements tell us how fast and economical the car is and we can compare one car with another, if the measurements have been made in exactly the same way for every car. If they haven't we might be disappointed when we drive away from the showroom. We might buy seven large apples or ten small apples at the supermarket, for the same price. It is the mass of the apples we have bought, not the number, that fixes the price we pay for the bagful. Big apples cost more. When we buy a litre of orange juice we want just as much orange juice as the person queuing in a different shop 30 miles away. Trading standards officers ensure that the measurements made in the supermarket are the same in every shop and they compare their own weights with those in the National Weights and Measures Laboratory which, in turn, are based on those in the National Physical Laboratory.

These common examples show that we measure distance, time, volume and mass quite regularly without thinking twice. What was life like before we used so many measurements?

Before measurement

When Stonehenge was built there were no standards as we know them today, but each upright had to be the same length and had to be vertical. Simple! The two stones were placed alongside each other and the longer one was chiselled down to the right length. When the builders stood them up they used a plumb line to get them vertical.

ACTIVITY
How can you use a plumb line to make a device which will ensure that a table is horizontal? You need a standard horizontal surface.

Ensuring value for money is always important. Two thousand years ago the King of Greece bought a new gold crown. He suspected that he was being cheated and that it was not all gold but that there were other, cheaper, metals inside. He turned to his chief scientist, Archimedes, and asked him to find out. Archimedes was worried; he could not cut the crown in half and look. He could balance it on a pair of scales, but what volume of gold must he put in to the other pan of the balance? The volume of a shape as irregular as the crown could not be calculated; it would have to be measured. How could he find the exact volume of the crown to balance with the same volume of gold? Archimedes was still puzzling over the problem when he got into his bath and noticed that the level of the water rose and it finally overflowed; it would have overflowed more as he lay back in it. Archimedes realised that this was the answer to his problem. The resulting 'streak' is legendary.

ACTIVITY
1. Explain how Archimedes' bath gave him the idea of how to measure the density of the crown.
2. How would he have known if the King had been cheated?

Archimedes.

Not all discoveries have been so revealing, but over the passage of time each community has developed its own standards. Captain Cook exchanged worthless beads and mirrors for gold but then the islanders genuinely thought they were getting a good deal as well; both sides were happy.

Measurement is a practical activity and units were invented which would mean the same to somebody on the next island or in the next village.

Captain Cook.

Stonehenge.

Life becomes more complicated

Imagine that you are living in a village in the 15th century. What measurements would you make if you wanted to sell your horse to someone in the next village?

How useful is this horse of yours? You would describe how tall it is; you might use the palms of your hands held sideways (be careful to include your thumb) and put one on top of the other from the ground up to the horse's shoulder. We still use the measurement called 'the hand' to describe the height of a horse, but now it has been standardised to four inches (10.16 cm). The furlong was the distance an average horse could pull a plough without stopping to rest – you could point out that the horse you are selling would pull at least two furlongs!

The size of a field was measured in acres. One acre was the area which a team of oxen could plough in one day. A farmer could work out roughly how long it would take him to help his neighbour do the ploughing with both of his oxen.

Other units of length have been used and discarded. The span is the distance between the thumb and first finger of the outstretched hand, and the cubit was the distance from fingertip to elbow. Another was the yardstick, now replaced by the metre rule. These older measurements were not really very accurate because there has never been such a thing as the standard horse or the standard human body. So, all length measurements have been standardised on the metre; but how long is that?

Measurement now

The modern system of units is the *Système International* (or SI) and some of the standards are still kept at the Standards Bureau in Sèvres in France. There are seven fundamental quantities, of which mass, length, time, temperature and electric current are the most often used.

The SI unit for length is the metre, and this was defined as the distance between two marks on a piece of metal kept in Sèvres. This was then copied and sent to countries around the world; the National Physical Laboratory still has the UK's copy. This meant, of course, that you would have had to go to Sèvres for an exact comparison with the original. This was too inconvenient; an absolute standard which could be made and calibrated anywhere in the world was obviously needed.

In 1960, light was used to define the metre. Light in a vacuum travels at the same speed anywhere in the universe. So, the metre became defined as the distance travelled (in a vacuum) by light in a very precise period of time. This seems rather complicated, but the great advantage is that scientists anywhere in the world can make their own standard of length accurately and to the same definition as others.

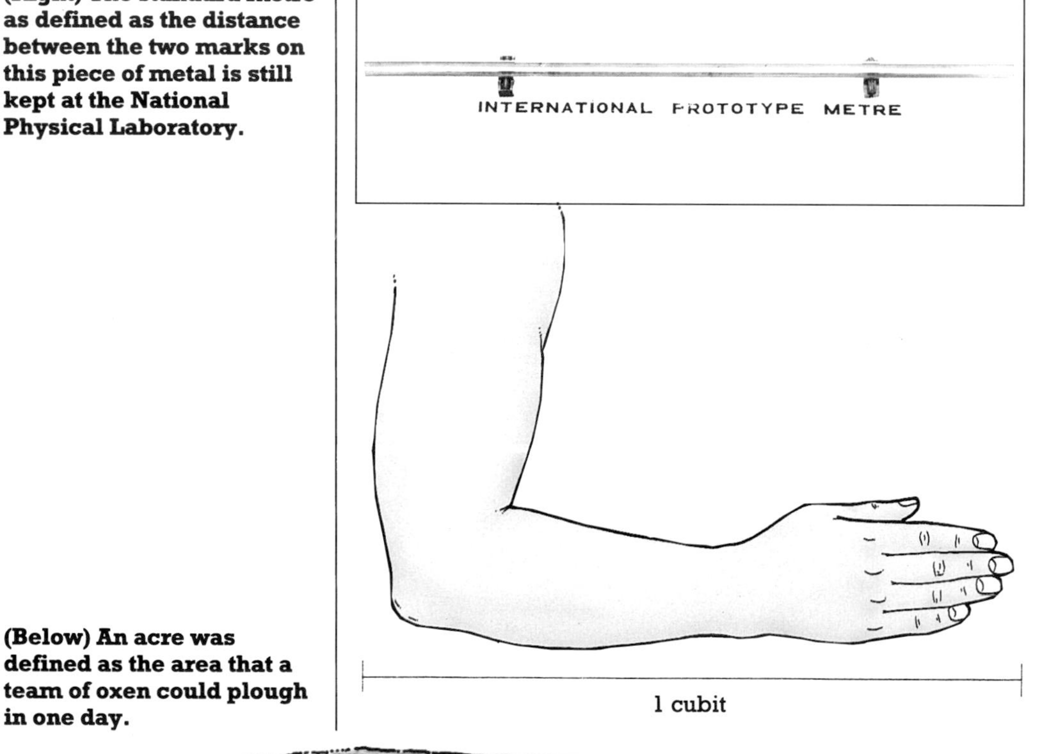

(Right) The standard metre as defined as the distance between the two marks on this piece of metal is still kept at the National Physical Laboratory.

(Below) An acre was defined as the area that a team of oxen could plough in one day.

Metre length, as defined by light, using laser apparatus at the National Physical Laboratory

▼

Calibration of laser apparatus at the National Weights and Measures Laboratory

▼

Production of calibration equipment and machinery to duplicate the metre length

▼

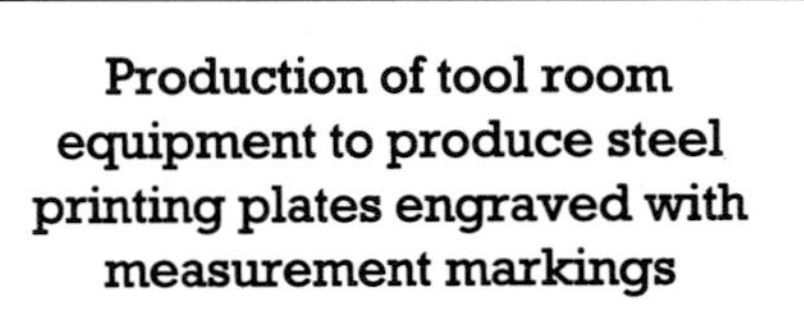

Production of tool room equipment to produce steel printing plates engraved with measurement markings

▼

Printing of ruler gradations on moulded plastic strips to produce plastic rulers

A much simplified flow chart to show the steps involved in ruler manufacture.

ACTIVITY
1. Explain why the standard mass is kept in a vacuum (this is a question for chemists).
2. Match the 7 fundamental quantities to their SI units, eg 2 – F.

QUANTITY	SI UNIT
1. Mass	A. Second
2. Length	B. Mole
3. Time	C. Kilogram
4. Electric current	D. Kelvin
5. Temperature	E. Candela
6. Amount of substance	F. Metre
7. Luminous intensity	G. Ampere

Weight is the force of gravity on a body. The more mass a body possesses, the greater is its weight, because the Earth attracts it with more force. Pictures of astronauts on the Earth show men lumbering around, literally weighed down by all their equipment, yet on the Moon they can jump high off the ground. The reason is that the Moon has much less mass and so attracts the astronauts with less force. Thus, they 'weigh' less. Gravity also gets less strong the further you are from the centre of the earth. So, a bag of apples would weigh less on top of Mount Everest than it does at sea level.

Weight is of no use as a fundamental standard, and so, for a precise measurement of how much 'stuff' a body is made of, we must use mass. The mass of an apple doesn't change – until you take a bite out of it!

Thc unit of mass is the kilogram and this is still defined as the mass of a particular piece of metal (platinum-iridium alloy) kept in a vacuum chamber in Sèvres. The National Physical Laboratory keeps the British copy of this at Teddington. Comparisons with our copy are reasonably easy – a simple method is to balance its weight against the weight of the unknown mass.

Big and small

In this chapter we have looked at how measurements have been made down the years and why standard measurements are required. In the rest of the book we shall look at the way in which measurement is applied and at the wide variety of measurements which need to be standardised. The metre is a useful everyday length but imagine using a metre rule to measure the distance from London to Edinburgh or the thickness of a human hair. Once the standard has been set, a wide variety of instruments are needed for practical measurements.

ACTIVITY
How would you measure:
a) the distance from London to Edinburgh,
b) the thickness of a human hair?

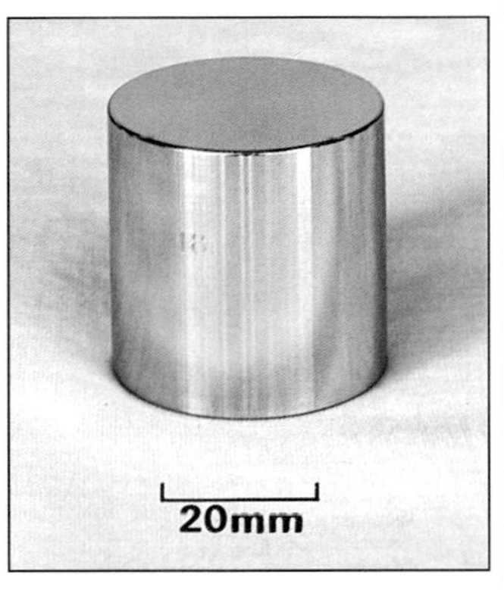

The piece of platinum iridium alloy that is the standard kg.

This man weighs less on the moon because the moon has less mass than the Earth and attracts the astronaut with less force.

2: BUILDING ON MEASUREMENT

To build a bridge so that we can transport heavy loads across a large river we must first measure how wide the river is and we must know how heavy the load is going to be. We can then do some experiments on a small scale with our building materials – ie build a model. When we know how the materials behave we can build our bridge. But, as you can see from the pictures of the two bridges across the Firth of Forth, there is more than one way to solve this problem.

In the 80 years between the first design and the second design, engineers had obviously radically changed their ideas about bridges. The rail bridge contains a lot of metal and is very heavy; it needs almost constant painting to keep it free from rust and the supports must carry a huge weight compared to the weight of the load – a train. There are many other problems with such a complex structure. The road bridge is a much more simple concept but only possible because we now know much more about our materials.

When we do build our structure the materials must be made to the standards that were used in the design model. The concrete must compress to just the correct amount and the steel wires must only stretch as much as we expect, or the roadway will be unusable. Standards in materials technology are just as important as absolute standards of measurement.

(Below)
The Forth road bridge.

(Bottom)
The Forth rail bridge.

When do things break?

You can break a cotton thread by pulling too hard; a steel wire can also be broken by pulling in the same way but with a lot more force. A steel wire will stretch a lot before it breaks, but when too great a load is applied it will snap. Before it breaks it will become permanently deformed. If you take a coiled spring you can straighten it out before it breaks, but it will not coil itself up again, and it has become useless as a spring. Similarly, a clockwork spring must not be overwound or it will remain tightly coiled and will not drive the clock. The ability of a material to return to its original shape is called the elasticity of that material. Bridges and buildings must be designed so that they retain the same shape; in other words, the materials must remain elastic.

A springboard is elastic – when the diver stands on the end the board bends a large amount, yet when he or she dives off, it returns to its original shape ready for the next diver. But when the same person stands on a concrete floor you do not notice the floor bending. This is because the concrete floor is very much stiffer. A good way to show this is by using graphs.

Suppose we have two springs, **A** and **B**. We hang weights from the end and measure how much longer they get. From graph 1 on the right we can see that when the same load is used on both springs, spring **B** gets much longer than spring **A**. We can say that spring **A** is stiffer than spring **B**.

ACTIVITY

Two identical springs will both be identical to spring A in the graph on the right when their elastic behaviour is measured. They can be connected in series as in arrangement (1), or in parallel, as in arrangement (2). When the elastic behaviour of (1) and (2) is measured, which arrangement produces line **P** and which arrangement line **Q** in graph 2 (bottom right)?

In neither case can we tell from these graphs how much more load the springs can take before they lose their elasticity and become permanently deformed. This is called exceeding the elastic limit. Before we can use materials we must measure their behaviour very thoroughly. The National Physical Laboratory has done this very accurately using its standards of mass, length and time and engineers consult the data the NPL has produced before using materials in their designs.

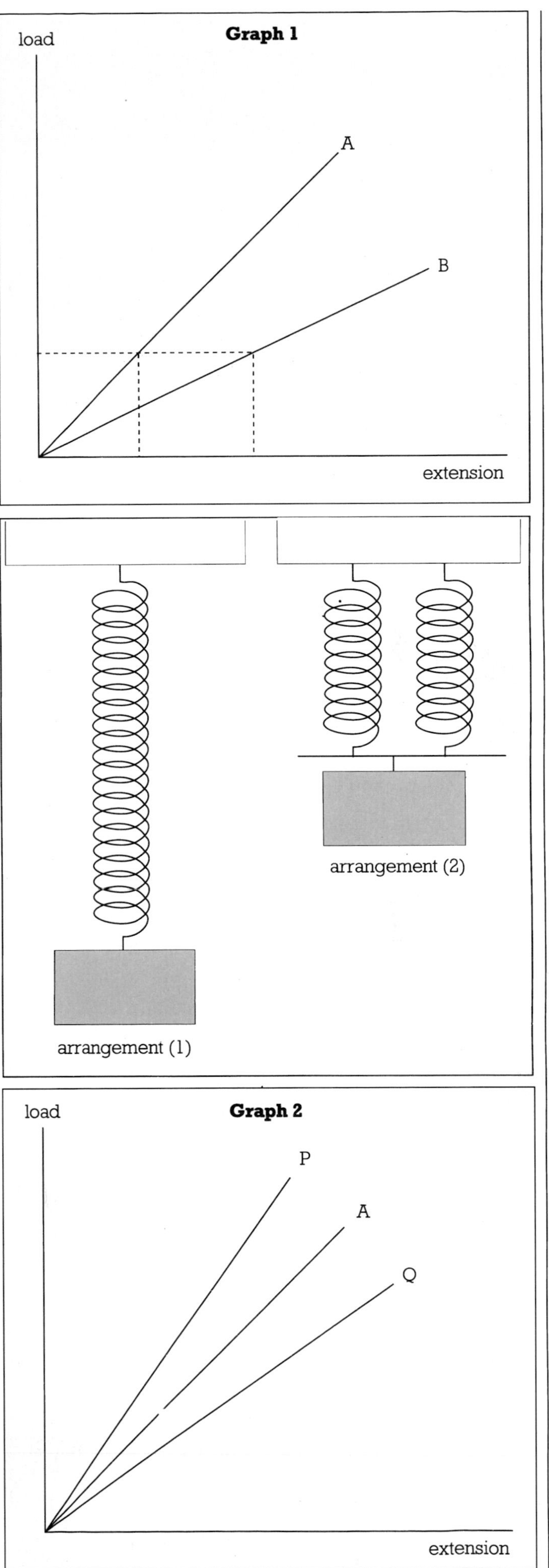

(Left) A springboard is elastic – it bends when the diver stands on the end of it and returns to being horizontal when the diver jumps off.

Tension and compression

When a structure is built there are many parts of it in compression. Think of the foundations of the National Westminster Tower in London, they have to support the whole weight of the building above them. A dam is built from concrete, and the deeper down in the water, the greater is the pressure of water on the dam – this is why dams are thicker at the bottom. The concrete can resist this sideways force because the weight of the concrete above causes so much compression – try pulling a playing card from a pack which is being tightly gripped to see the same effect. The further down the dam goes the more weight of concrete there is above and so the more able the dam is to resist the greater force of the water. Concrete is very strong when it is in compression and is excellent for making dams.

ACTIVITY

1. Compare the behaviour of the two materials **A** and **B**. Assume that they both break when the graph ends.
2. Why is material **B** suitable for making wires for electric cables?

load

A

B

extension

The Benevean dam.

Beams

In order to make a building with rooms in it the structure must contain beams which support the floor above. The beams are elastic and deform when a load is put on them. As you can see from the diagram below, the top surface of a bending beam is in compression and the bottom surface is in tension. The top surface is being made shorter because it is on the inside of the curve; the spider on the top surface has less far to travel than the spider underneath. The middle of the beam does not change in length.

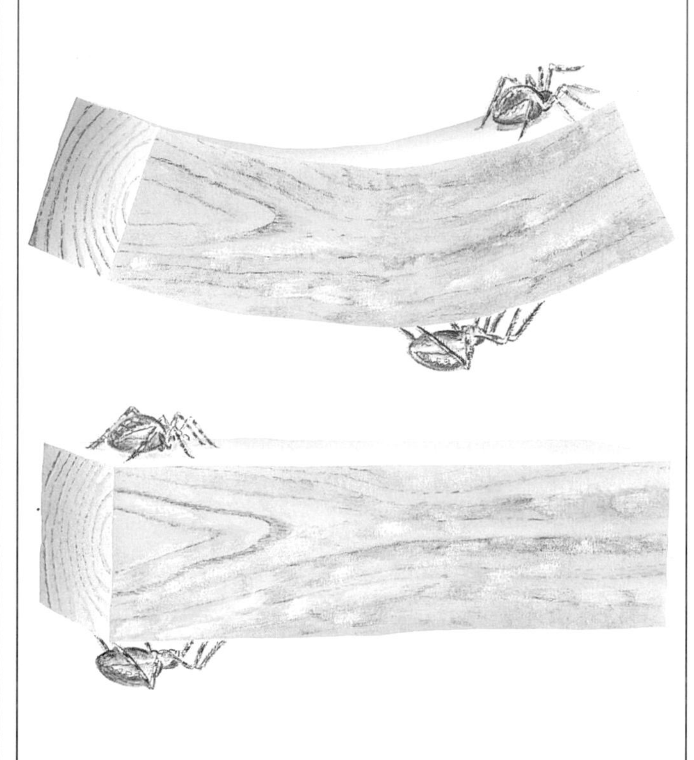

ACTIVITY

Take a ruler in both hands and try to bend it. It is easy to bend when your thumbs are on the flat surface. Now try bending it by putting your thumbs on the edge.

If a beam is made thicker then it is more difficult to bend – it is stiffer and more able to withstand a load. A joist is a piece of wood which supports a floor, and it is usually made in an oblong shape. This shape is used with the long sides vertical. This means that for the same weight of wood, more load can be supported and the whole floor structure is lighter. The walls therefore have less weight to support and the building is safe. This is a simple example of materials technology.

Shaped structures

Steel joists are used when making bigger structures because steel is a stronger material than wood, and so the span or length of the beam can be longer. A common shape for a beam is an I shape. In this shape the 'flange' at the top and the bottom carry most of the load and the web simply connects the two flanges and stops them sliding over each other. The middle of the beam is not stretched at all.

Steel joists hanging from a crane on a construction site.

Shell/Esso production platform Brent D is a concrete gravity structure which operates in the North Sea at a depth of 142 m.

A floating oil rig is an example of a structure which must be very strong and as light as possible. It must be light enough to float and yet strong enough to withstand gale-force winds and big waves. The oil rig legs are hollow tubes with internal bracing. The construction of the legs is a complex operation but it provides a solution to the problem. In the same way the Channel Tunnel has been designed as a tube for greater strength.

There are many examples where the shape of a structure adds strength. A body panel of a car can be made stronger by putting a crease across it or by shaping it into a curve. Once the metal has been shaped it has lost much of its elasticity and will no longer flex. So, after shaping, it is heated in an oven for some hours and this heat treatment restores its elastic properties so that the shaped panel now behaves like the original metal but has the added strength of its new shape.

ACTIVITY

1. Take an ordinary piece of file paper and stand it on its end. It falls over. Fold it in half and open it out like a book. It now stands up – you have made a very simple structure. See how strong you can make a single piece of paper (hint – think of corrugated iron).
2. Take a newspaper, 2 m of sticky tape and an ordinary brick. Make a structure which will support the brick above the ground. Think of an oil rig. You can have a competition to see who can support the brick highest off the ground.

The graph drawn in the Activity box on page 10 shows two different materials. **A** is a brittle material and **B** is called a ductile material. Although **A** is very stiff it will not support much load before it snaps and neither will it extend very far; we say that **A** is not a strong material. Standard methods of testing have been established which can provide accurate values of strength. Such precise measurements and standards are used at the NPL to provide this essential information not only on traditional materials like steel, iron and concrete, but also on an increasing range of new materials such as plastics and ceramics.

Composite materials

Back to the beam. In modern buildings many of the structural members are made of concrete because it is a very easy material to make into the right shape; it is simply poured into a container and when it becomes hard the container is removed. It is also very strong in compression and we have seen that there are many compressive loads in a structure – in a dam for example. Unfortunately, concrete is very weak in tension; it simply cracks. This is because concrete is an aggregate of small particles held together in a matrix of cement which 'sets' like a glue. So a concrete beam will start to crack where it is in tension, on its lower surface. Similarly vertical members or columns will crack when subject to a side loading from the wind.

The solution is to insert a material into the concrete beam which is strong in tension. The reinforcing material most often used is steel, and a network of steel rods is laid out before the concrete beam is made. The cement holds the steel in place and the finished composite beam has the desired properties of both concrete and steel. There are many composite materials that have properties which are different from their constituent materials.

Another frequently used composite is fibreglass. Thin glass fibres are very strong in tension but are too flexible to be of any use as a structure. A matting of these fibres is made, with the fibres lined up in many different directions, and the whole is embedded in a matrix of plastic resin. The resin hardens and when the resulting composite sheet bends there are always fibres of glass lying in the right direction to take the tensile load. If the direction in which force is to be applied to a structure is known then even stronger materials, such as carbon fibres, can be put into the matrix, making a material which is both very light and very strong.

Applications include helicopter blades, artificial limbs and sports equipment such as squash racquets, golf clubs or fishing rods. Aircraft and Formula One racing cars make extensive use of composite materials which can be designed for specific uses.

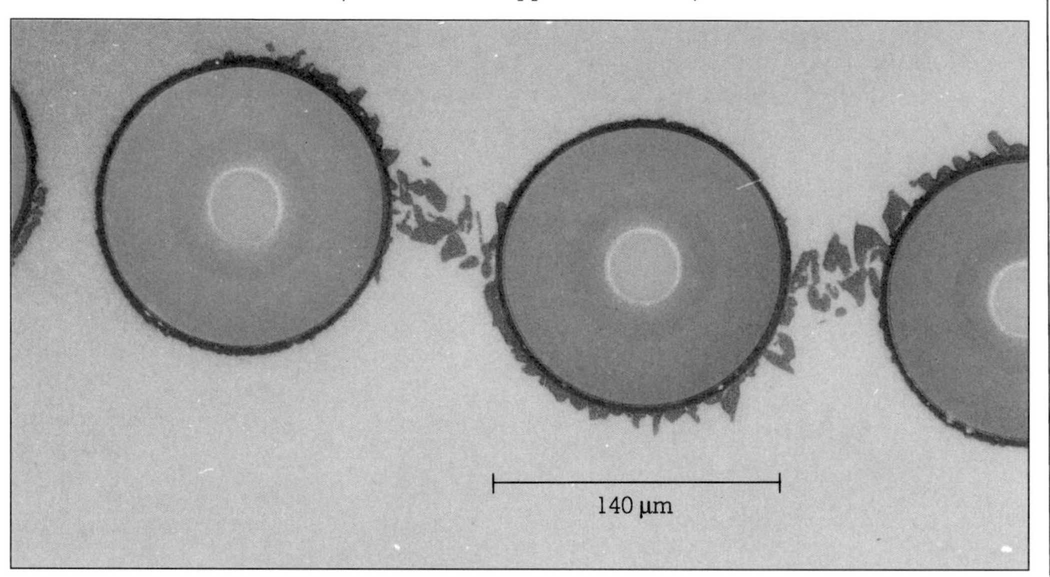

(Right) A cross-section through a carbon fibre reinforced titanium alloy.

(Below) Formula one racing.

Composite structures can be very light indeed whilst retaining great strength. Aircraft floors can be made in the following way. Two sheets of glass fibre-reinforced epoxy resin are held one centimetre apart by a honeycomb made of very thin resin-impregnated aramid sheeting placed on edge. The honeycomb is glued to the sheets. This combines two properties which we have already mentioned. The upper and lower sheets take much of the bending load, like the flanges of an I beam, whilst the aramid sheeting is very strong edgeways when it has been shaped and placed on edge – see the Activity on page 11.

The Beech Starship – constructed from composite materials.

glass fibre reinforced epoxy resin

resin-impregnated aramid honeycomb core

The structure of the composite material used in aircraft flooring.

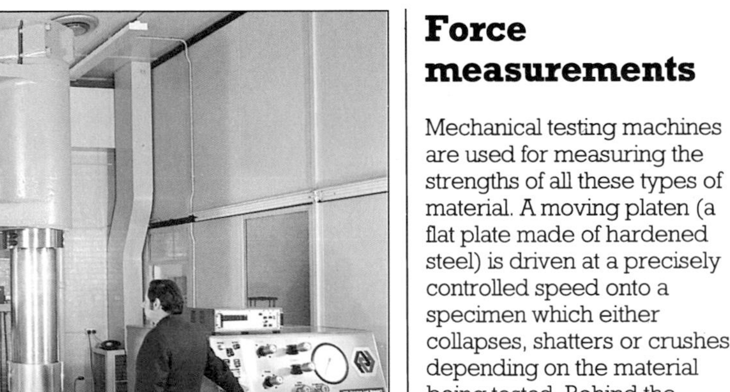

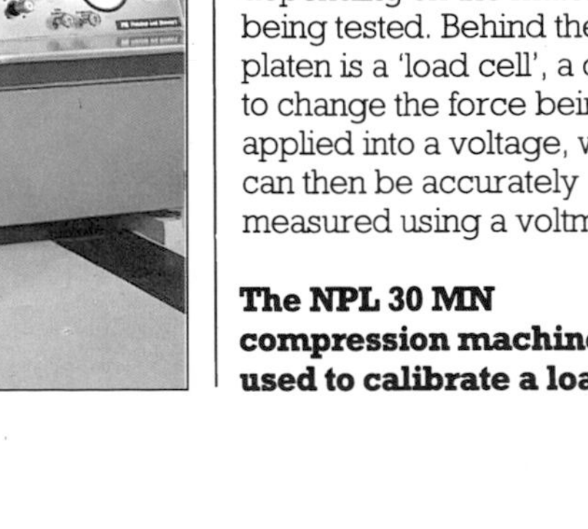

The NPL 30 MN compression machine being used to calibrate a load cell.

Force measurements

Mechanical testing machines are used for measuring the strengths of all these types of material. A moving platen (a flat plate made of hardened steel) is driven at a precisely controlled speed onto a specimen which either collapses, shatters or crushes, depending on the material being tested. Behind the platen is a 'load cell', a device to change the force being applied into a voltage, which can then be accurately measured using a voltmeter.

The load cell must first be calibrated by measuring its voltage output against a series of precisely known forces. The NPL provides a customer service for the precise measurement of load cells and issues complete calibration information. Its standard for calibration forces is based on the primary standard of mass, the kilogram, maintained at NPL. The NPL compression testing machine shown is the only equipment in Europe capable of measuring up to 30 MN (30 000 000 newtons) with an accuracy of ± 0.1%.

The size of the specimen tested must also be measured with high precision for the accurate calculation of the strength of the material.

3: COLOUR CODING

'Any colour, so long as it's black' – *Henry Ford.*

The fact that black isn't a colour would not bother a man with such straightforward opinions as Henry Ford. But how can we have black paint when we can't have black light? In this chapter we shall be investigating colour; how we use it and if we can possibly measure it.

Light

Light and the absence of light are sensations which enabled us to function as predatory animals, and our control of light is some measure of our civilisation. We can see the Sun or a light-bulb because they both emit light – they are said to be incandescent. We see all other physical objects because they reflect light. The Sun actually emits energy over a huge range of frequencies in the electromagnetic spectrum, but a narrow range of these frequencies excite certain cells at the back of our eyes and we call this range 'visible light'.

While Sir Isaac Newton was waiting for the apples on his tree to ripen he noticed sunlight coming through a hole in the window blind. He placed a glass prism in the light beam and saw on the wall opposite that the light was no longer a white beam but had spread out into a spectacular range of colour. He called it a spectrum and recorded the colours in the order red, orange, yellow, green, blue, indigo, violet. 'Richard Of York Gave Battle In Vain' or ROYGBIV, is a phrase that might help you to remember the order.

When light travels through glass it slows down, and so it changes direction at the boundary (the exception to this is when light hits the glass boundary at a 90 degree angle). In a prism different colours travelling at slightly different speeds pass through the glass, and the direction of each colour is changed by a slightly different amount so that the colours are separated. In fact, each colour is a different wavelength of light which produces a slightly different reaction in our eye. When we see the continuous range of wavelengths we see 'white light'.

Additive colour mixing using lamps.

Adding and subtracting

Just as white light can be separated into its constituent colours, so it can be added together again. Suppose we take three stage lanterns and cover one with a green filter, one with a red filter and one with a blue filter and then aim the three circles onto a white screen so that they overlap. We see the colours shown in the diagram. These are the three primary colours and when added together they make white light because they are **sources** of light. A filter absorbs all the light and transmits its own colour so that the light falling on the screen is pure red, pure green and pure blue. These colours then add together to form the colours shown. Blackness is simply an absence of light.

If an object has been painted, then we see it by reflected light, not transmitted light. Thus the pigment in primary magenta paint absorbs all the colours that fall onto it and reflects magenta light, so we see it as magenta; the cyan pigment reflects cyan light and yellow reflects only yellow. Thus, if we mix paint together, all the colours are absorbed by one of the pigments and there is none left to reflect. If there is no reflected light we say that the surface is black.

A scene from Cats – the acclaimed London show.

So, the colours of paints are colours by subtraction, and if you take everything away, the result is no reflected light – or blackness. So we have black paint but not black light.

ACTIVITY
1. Name the secondary colours in both colour wheels.
2. What happens when a primary colour and its complementary colour are added?

Subtractive colour mixing using paints or inks.

Seeing colour

There are three factors which affect the colour you see:
1. The pigment of the object.
2. The colour (or colours) of the light illuminating it.
3. The observer – you.

ACTIVITY
The pigment of an object determines which wavelengths are reflected, and the colour of the light determines which wavelengths hit an object. Paint a box with pure magenta-coloured paint (red and blue added together). If you illuminate one side of the box with primary red then that side will appear red – there is no blue light for the magenta pigment to reflect. Now illuminate the opposite side with primary blue, then that side will appear blue since there is no red light for the pigment to reflect. Now turn the box round. The red side becomes blue!

Theatrical lighting designers have been using reflected light for years. To light a musical some lights have red filters, some blue and some yellow, and some are white. The effect is that the colours of all the costumes appear very vivid because they all have their own colour shining on them, and the overall effect is bright and cheerful. Similarly, plays with a gloomy mood might be lit with green light, although this makes the actors themselves look rather ill. Colour has a great psychological effect on us and painters and advertisers use this to the full.

This brings us to the third factor – the observer. The colour you call green is almost certainly different to the colour your friend calls green. The reason for this is that your eye and brain are different from your friend's.

ACTIVITY
Try to agree with a friend on a description of five different shades of green. Green is a good colour to choose because it is the colour that the eye is most sensitive to. Why is this?

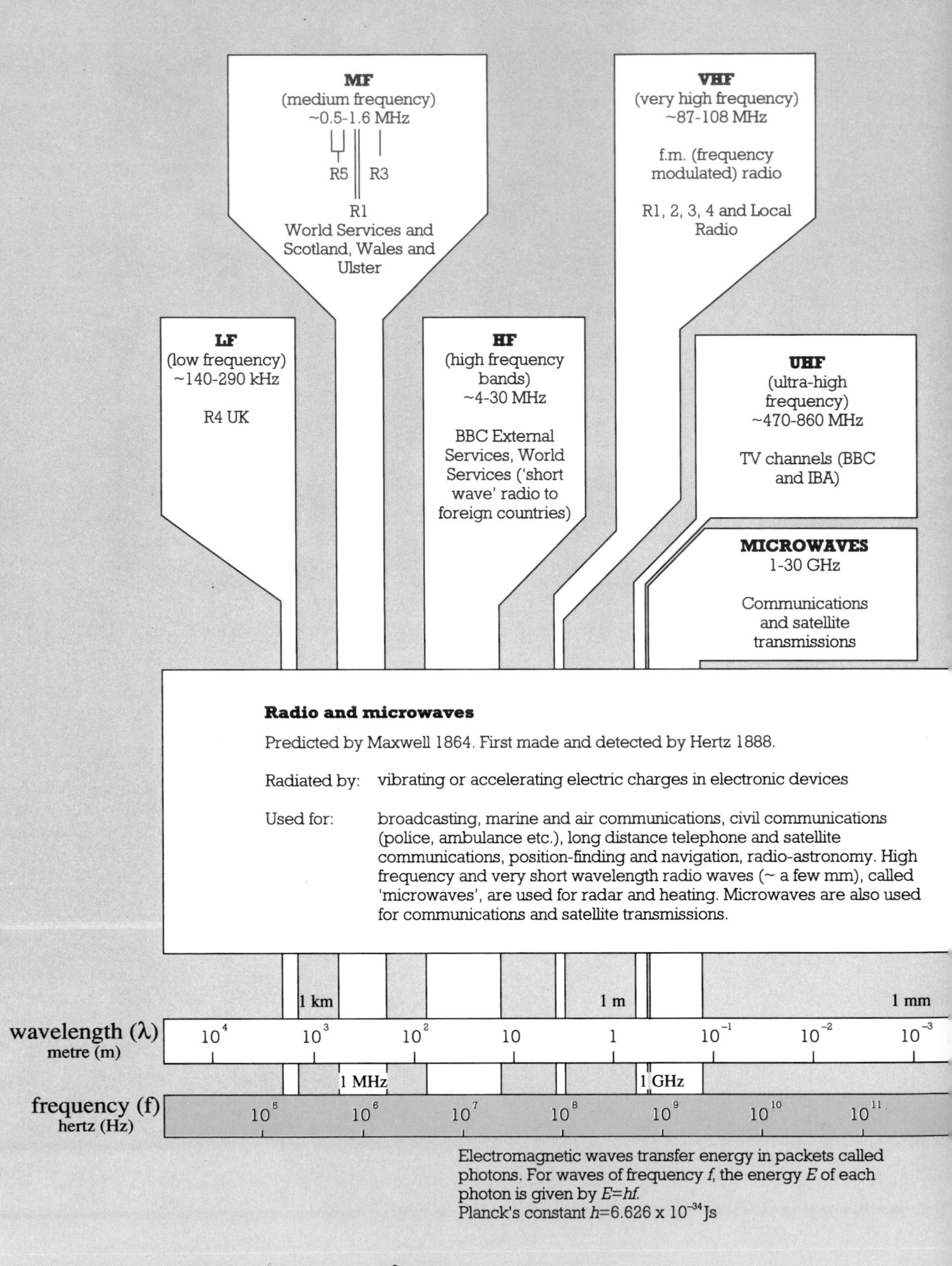

frequency × wavelength = speed $f\lambda = s$

speed = 3×10^8 m/s for all electromagnetic waves travelling in free space, usually represented by c.

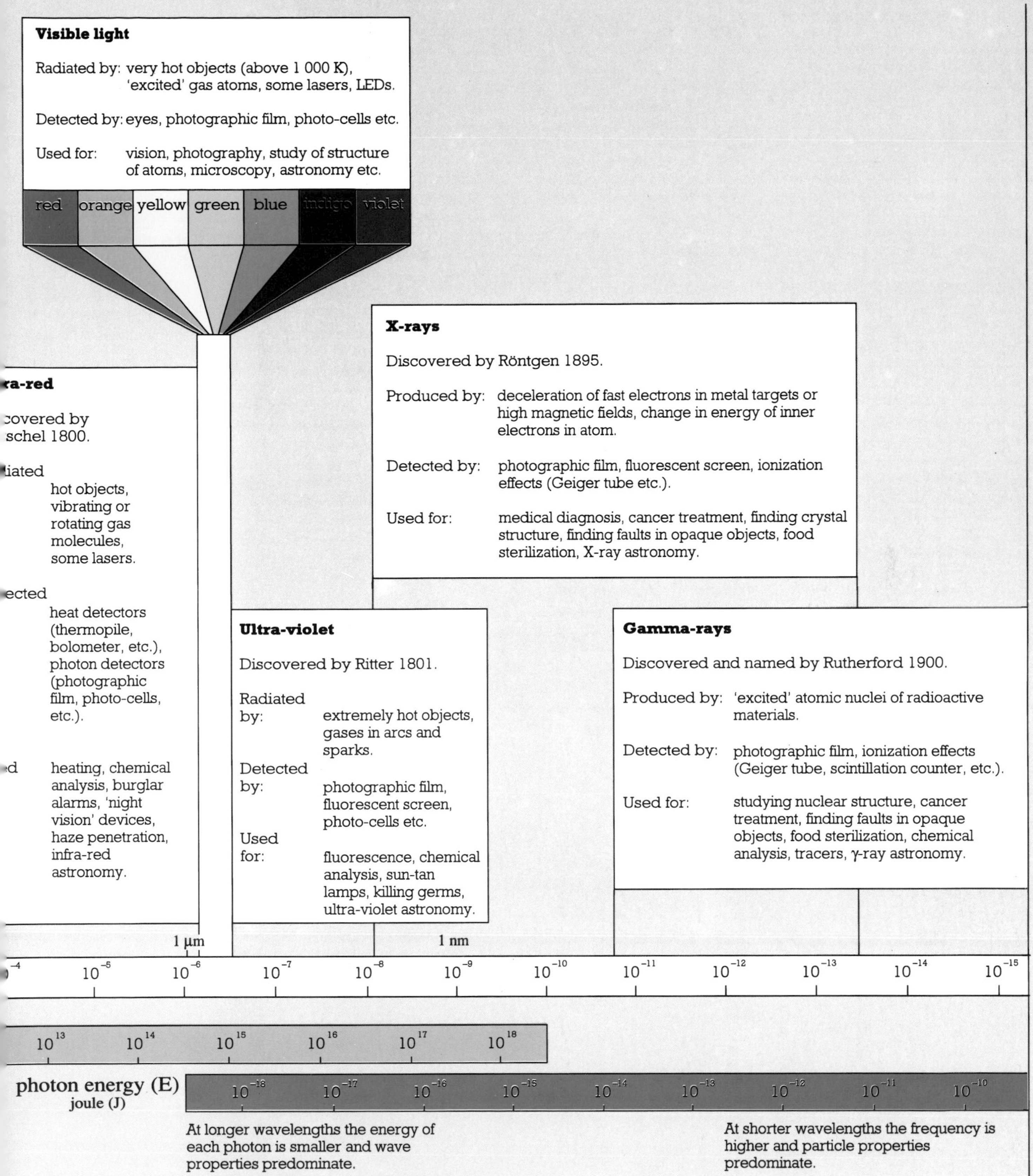

Visible light

Radiated by: very hot objects (above 1 000 K), 'excited' gas atoms, some lasers, LEDs.

Detected by: eyes, photographic film, photo-cells etc.

Used for: vision, photography, study of structure of atoms, microscopy, astronomy etc.

red | orange | yellow | green | blue | indigo | violet

...ra-red

...covered by ...schel 1800.

...iated hot objects, vibrating or rotating gas molecules, some lasers.

...ected heat detectors (thermopile, bolometer, etc.), photon detectors (photographic film, photo-cells, etc.).

...d heating, chemical analysis, burglar alarms, 'night vision' devices, haze penetration, infra-red astronomy.

X-rays

Discovered by Röntgen 1895.

Produced by: deceleration of fast electrons in metal targets or high magnetic fields, change in energy of inner electrons in atom.

Detected by: photographic film, fluorescent screen, ionization effects (Geiger tube etc.).

Used for: medical diagnosis, cancer treatment, finding crystal structure, finding faults in opaque objects, food sterilization, X-ray astronomy.

Ultra-violet

Discovered by Ritter 1801.

Radiated by: extremely hot objects, gases in arcs and sparks.

Detected by: photographic film, fluorescent screen, photo-cells etc.

Used for: fluorescence, chemical analysis, sun-tan lamps, killing germs, ultra-violet astronomy.

Gamma-rays

Discovered and named by Rutherford 1900.

Produced by: 'excited' atomic nuclei of radioactive materials.

Detected by: photographic film, ionization effects (Geiger tube, scintillation counter, etc.).

Used for: studying nuclear structure, cancer treatment, finding faults in opaque objects, food sterilization, chemical analysis, tracers, γ-ray astronomy.

1 μm   1 nm

10^{-4} 10^{-5} 10^{-6} 10^{-7} 10^{-8} 10^{-9} 10^{-10} 10^{-11} 10^{-12} 10^{-13} 10^{-14} 10^{-15}

10^{13} 10^{14} 10^{15} 10^{16} 10^{17} 10^{18}

photon energy (E) joule (J)

10^{-18} 10^{-17} 10^{-16} 10^{-15} 10^{-14} 10^{-13} 10^{-12} 10^{-11} 10^{-10}

At longer wavelengths the energy of each photon is smaller and wave properties predominate.

At shorter wavelengths the frequency is higher and particle properties predominate.

The electromagnetic spectrum

Looking at colour

Light is detected by the eye. By comparing the eye with a camera we shall see how both optical systems work.

ACTIVITY

Take a lens (15 cm convex) and hold it about 15 cm in front of a piece of white paper. Stand on the opposite side of the room to the window. Adjust the lens – paper distance until you form an image on the paper. Notice that it is upside-down or inverted. This is a very simple form of camera.

To work, both the eye and the camera must allow light to enter, and the light must be focused onto a surface which will register an image. The amount of light entering must be controlled and the whole device must be robust.

The camera has a lens cap and the eye has an eyelid. These protect the front from mechanical damage and are shut when the system is not in use – in our case when we are asleep. A camera may well have an almost clear filter to protect the lens from damage; the eye has a layer of tough transparent cells called the cornea, which does the same job. Inside the eye is a fluid called the aqueous humour; the camera has air inside. The aqueous humour lubricates and cleans the lens and the muscles and tissues as they move; the camera must be cleaned by the photographer by disassembling it – this would be difficult with your eye!

Both the camera and the eye have a lens which focuses the light onto a screen. They do this by bending or refracting the light. Both methods do the same job but in different ways, as we shall see later. To control the amount of light entering the system both the eye and the camera have an adjustable hole or aperture. The iris – or coloured part of the eye – has a hole in it which is called the pupil – the black centre of the eye. The pupil of the eye gets larger to allow more light in and is much smaller when the light is bright, and it is always circular. The aperture in a camera is controlled by a mechanical iris which is nearly circular.

The screen at the back of the system is covered with a light-sensitive material. In a camera this is a mixture of chemicals whose composition changes when exposed to light. They can only undergo this change once, and after the film has been exposed by the shutter (the length of time this is open also controls the amount of light entering the system) it must be removed from the system and developed chemically to produce the picture. The eye collects one image on the retina, passes the information to the brain down the optic nerve and the retina is then ready for the next image. This happens about seven times every second. The retina is coated with cells which convert the light to electrical energy by a rather complicated chemical process. The brain interprets these electrical signals as a picture of what you are looking at – you first learn how to do this as a very young baby.

Both optical systems are remarkably similar, but there are differences. In order to allow the image to fall on the retina, no matter how far away the object is, the lens must be adjusted. When relaxed the eye is focused at infinity, which means that, with perfect vision you can clearly see objects which are far away. The camera lens, by contrast, focuses on infinity when the lens is nearest to the film. When an object moves so that it is not in the place of the natural focus it becomes out of focus or fuzzy, and the lens must be adjusted.

A camera lens is brought into focus by turning the focusing ring. This would be a painful thing to have to do to your eyes! The lens in your eye focuses by changing shape. The eye lens is squashy – unlike the camera lens – and the ciliary muscles contract and make the lens fatter, which has the effect of focusing the light on the retina. So when you are reading, focusing on a close object, the ciliary muscles are working and your eyes get tired.

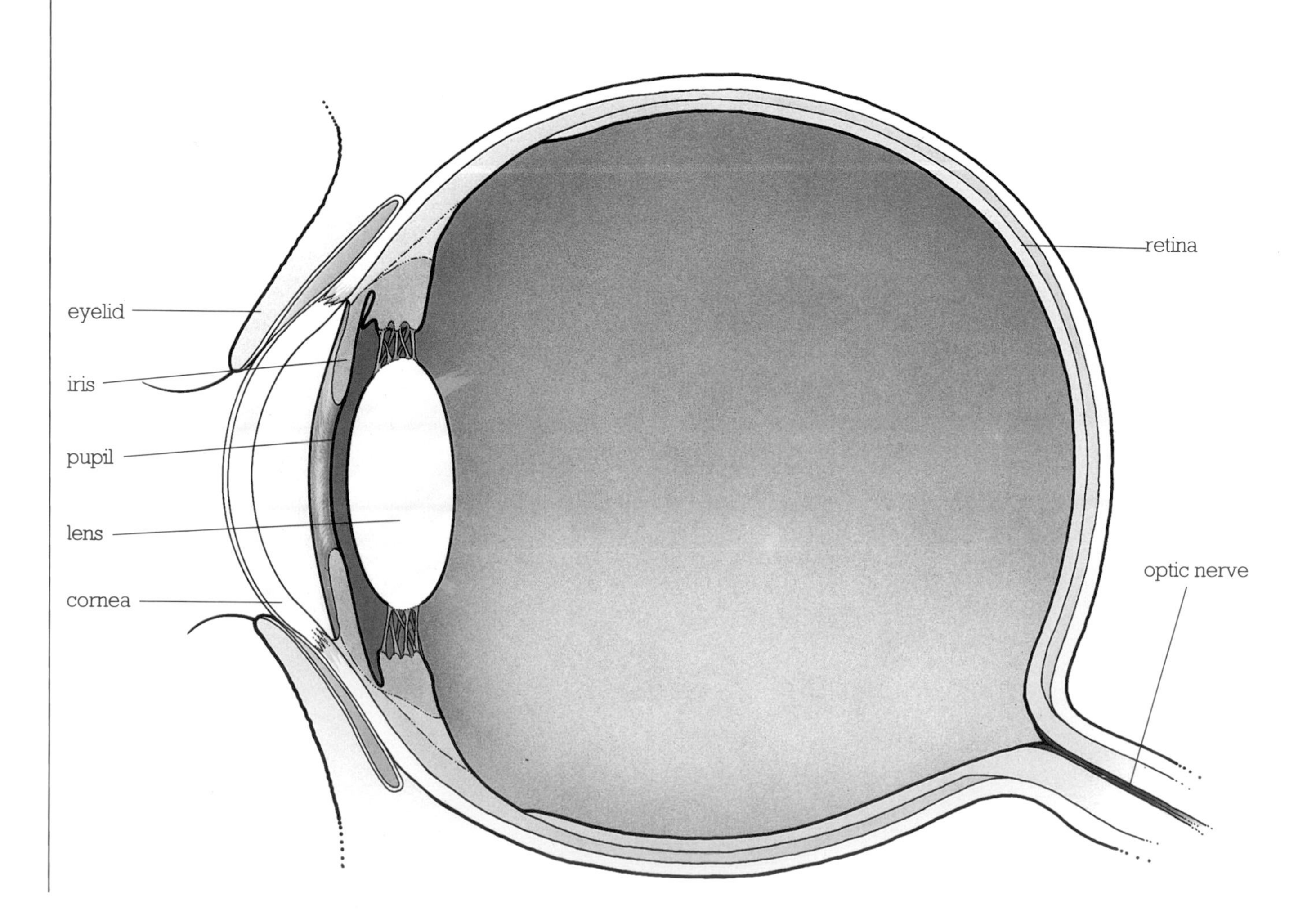

The eye only sees in the visible part of the spectrum; by changing the film in the camera we can take photographs using electromagnetic energy which the eye cannot see. For example, film which is sensitive to infra-red wavelengths enables us to take photographs in the dark. These images are caused by hot objects which radiate infra-red radiation. Pictures of the Earth taken in the infra-red spectrum from satellites can give a wealth of information about crops and land usage and are widely used in military applications such as for spotting hidden missile sites.

To photograph in black and white or colour we simply change the film. The eye has both types of film. Some cells in the retina called **rods** are very sensitive to light, but only detect the intensity of the light. Other cells, called **cones**, detect colour, and there are three types of these – one for each primary colour. So, an object reflecting magenta light will produce an image using the red and blue sensitive cones.

There are far more cones found near the centre of the retina and far more rods near the edge of the retina. Rods are used in peripheral vision – looking out of the corner of your eye. To see things better in very dim light look slightly away from what you want to see. The more sensitive rods will give your brain an image, although it will not be in colour.

ACTIVITY

Make a pinhole camera. Take a cardboard box (a shoe box would be good). Put black paper over one end and greaseproof paper over the other. Make a hole with a pin in the black paper and point this end at a bright object. On the greaseproof paper you will see an image. Why is it upside down?

The key to what you see is how your brain has learned to interpret the images sent down the optic nerves. We have all learned how to do this slightly differently and this is why we all see the same objects slightly differently. How do we know that we are even seeing the same things at all?

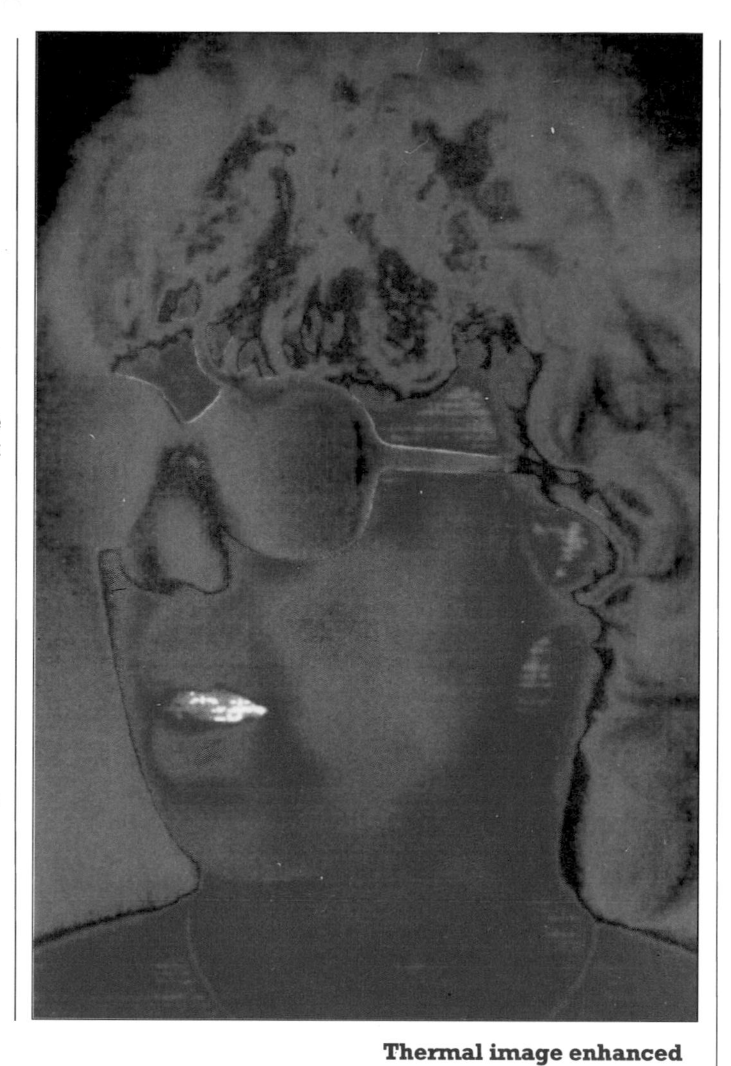

Thermal image enhanced with the NPL pseudo-colour scale, with white indicating the highest temperature.

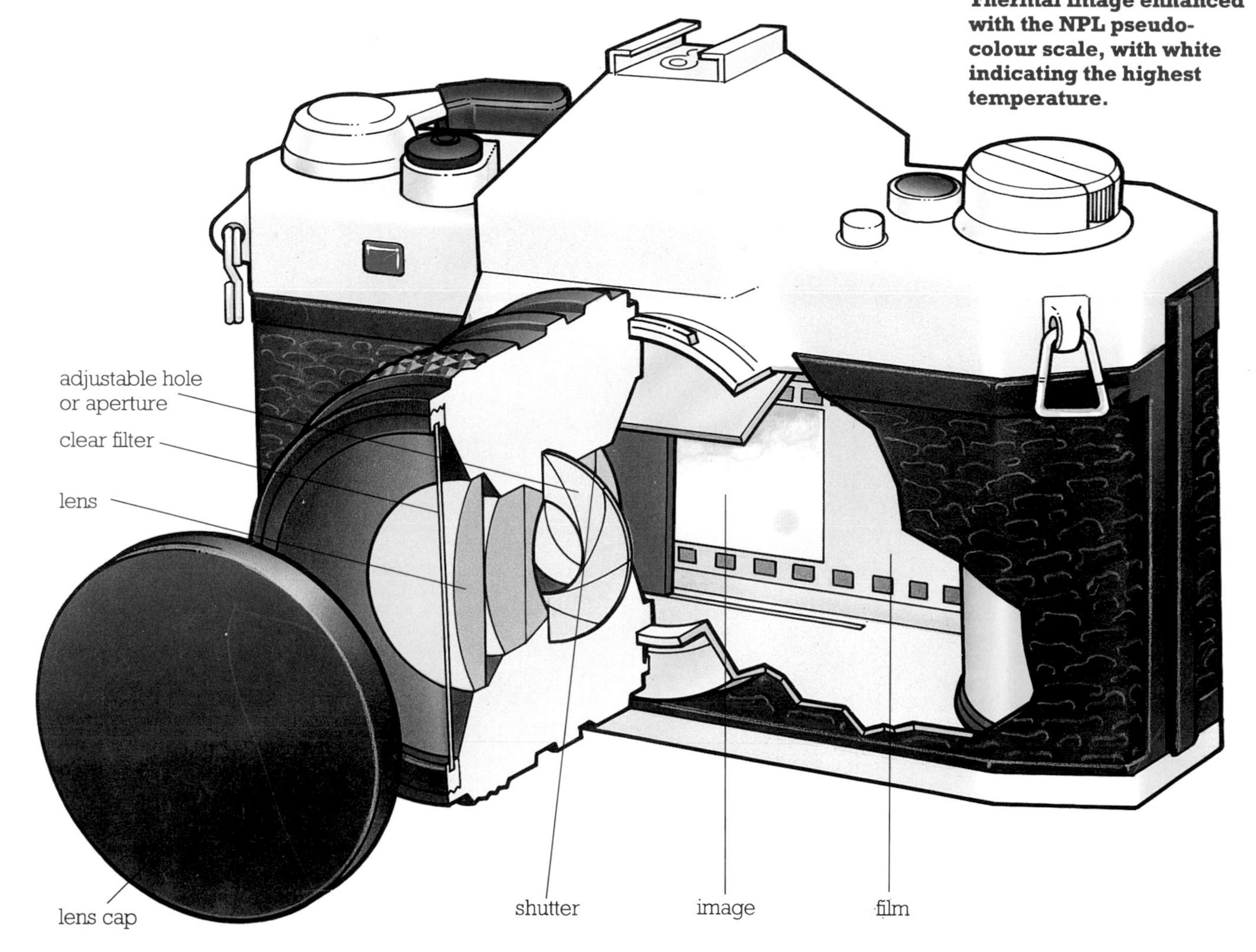

Measuring colour

If we all see different colours differently, how can we set a standard for colour?

When a gas is made hot the electrons in the atoms randomly absorb energy for a short time, and when they release it, it is emitted as a short pulse of light. There is a huge, countless number of atoms in even a small sample of gas, and so all these random pulses of light strike the eye and create the impression of continuous light. Since the atoms are all the same, the light has a characteristic colour. Some atoms emit only a few wavelengths; for example, sodium emits the yellow light seen in some street lamps. By taking a particular wavelength of light from a particular source we can identify a standard for colour.

When we split light into its separate wavelengths using a prism – or by using something called a diffraction grating – we can measure the wavelength of the light by measuring exactly how much it is deviated by the prism or grating. Thus, we can measure the wavelength of a particular colour without reference to what it looks like.

Much research has been done to determine how well the eye responds to different wavelengths, and standards determined by the NPL have greatly influenced the laws concerning vehicle and road lighting – it is no accident that many car dashboards have green lights. If you manufacture paint you need to be able to measure each batch and check that it is the same colour. Spectrophotometry is the tool used for this job and also to set standards for transmittance and reflectance so that one paint reflects as much light as another. If this were not done, some colours could appear brighter than others. Colour can be very complicated!

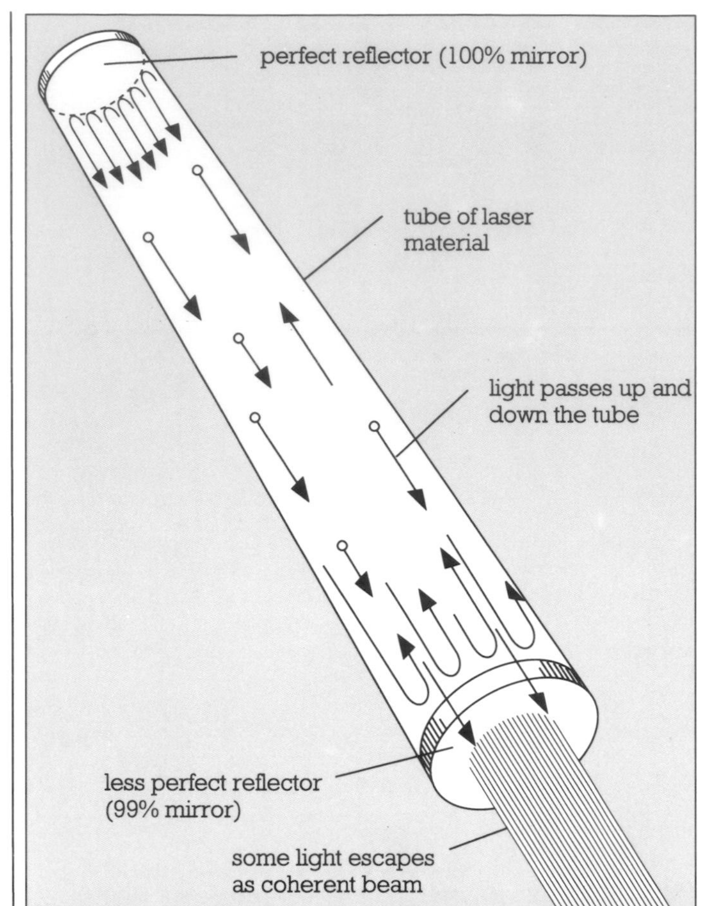

A diagram demonstrating the reflection of light within a laser.

Illuminated motorway sign and traffic lights on the M1 motorway. Advancing headlights on the right, receding tail-lights on the left.

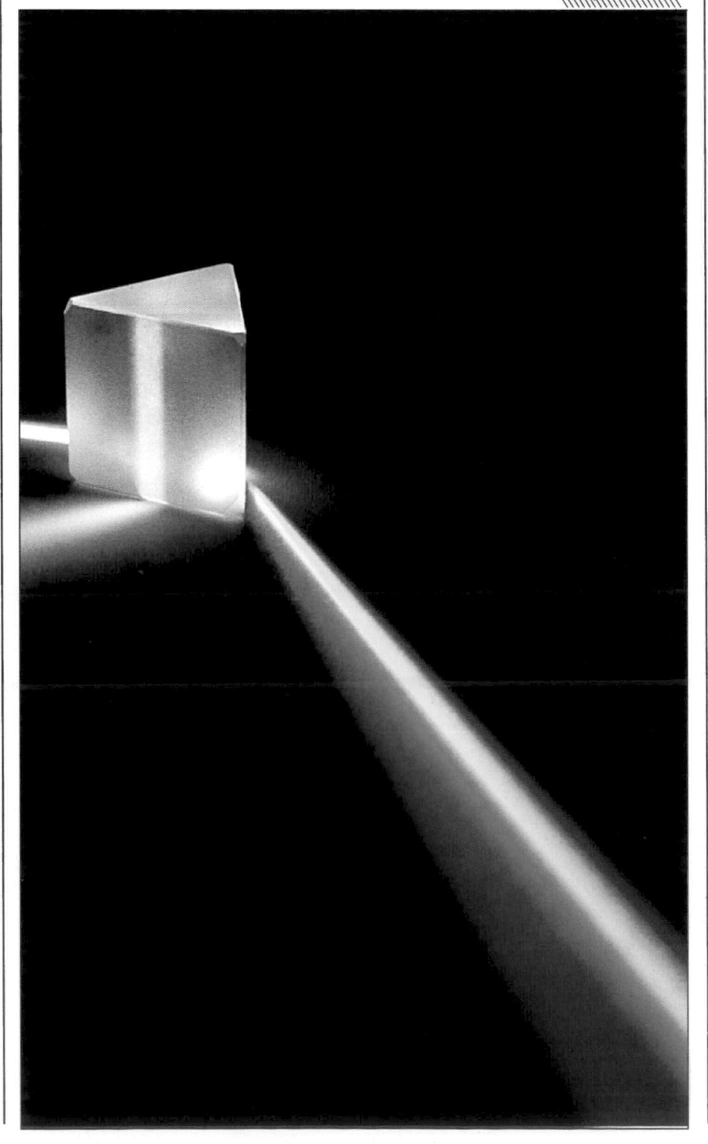

White light passing through a triangular prism to produce spectral colours.

Lasers

We have seen how atoms normally emit random pulses of light when their electrons absorb energy and lose it again. Normal light contains all these random pulses. Coherent light is achieved when all the pulses are emitted in phase with each other. Each atom is stimulated to emit its pulse in step with light which has already been emitted. Normal light is like a crowd of people walking across London Bridge; coherent light is like marching soldiers, each soldier in step with his neighbour.

The laser is the device which first produced coherent light in 1959. A tube containing suitable material – for example ruby or CO_2 – has two mirrors, one at each end; one mirror is a nearly perfect reflector, while the opposite mirror is a less perfect reflector. Light is passed up and down the tube and, in doing so, stimulates the atoms in the tube to emit light in phase with itself. Some light passes through the less perfect mirror and this is the coherent laser beam. The beam does not diverge and it also has a precisely determined wavelength and speed. These facts make it one of the most useful measuring tools ever invented. Lasers were used to ensure that the National Westminster Tower was built absolutely vertically.

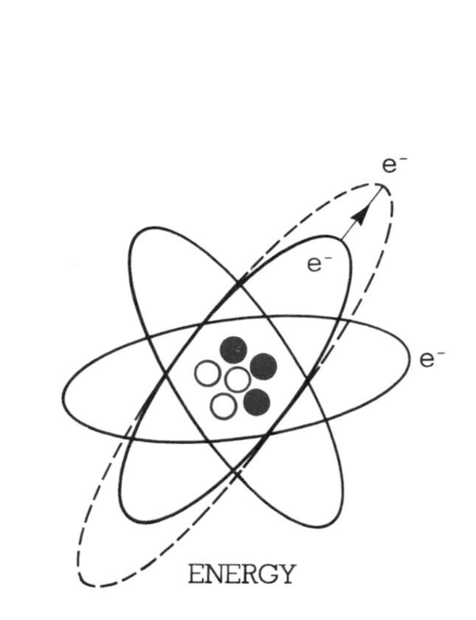

Electron absorbs energy and moves to a higher orbit.

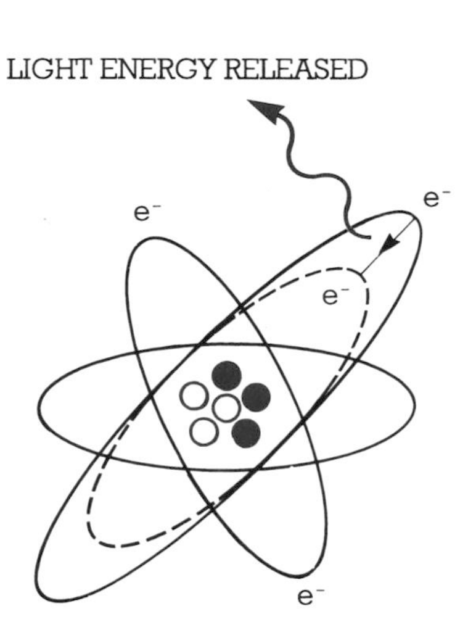

The electron returns to its ground state Light energy is released.

(Below Left) Two blue laser beams diverge from the stage at the Glastonbury pop festival 1983.

(Below) The National Westminster Tower.

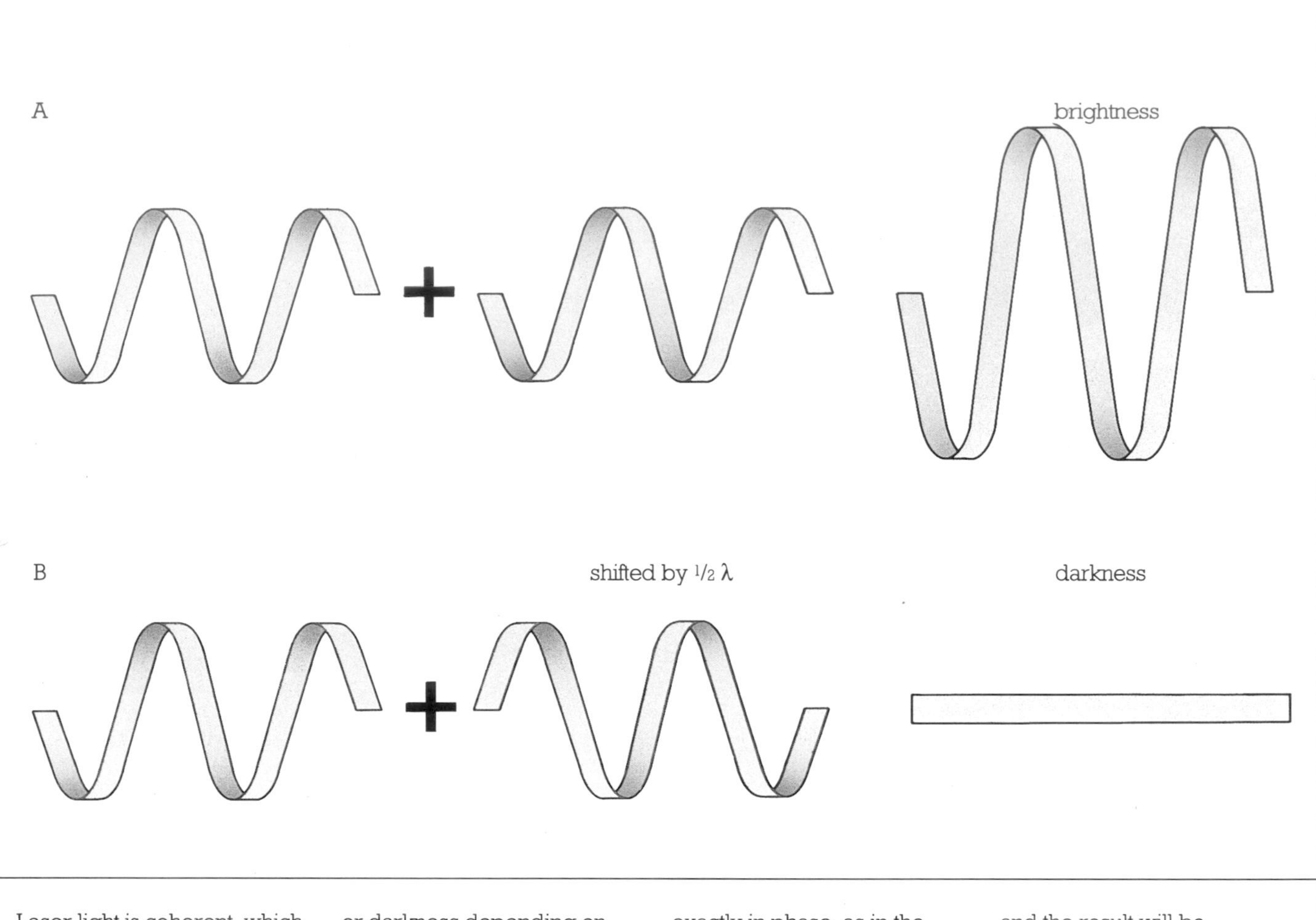

Laser light is coherent, which means that all the light is in phase, as in A in the diagram above. If laser light is reflected from a target and the reflection is added to a sample of the original, then the result will be brightness or darkness depending on the distance the light has travelled. Let us consider the addition. If the laser light travels an exact whole number of wavelengths (say 42 wavelengths), then the reflection and source will be exactly in phase, as in the diagram, and the result is brightness. If we move the target so that the light travels exactly half a wavelength further (42.5 wavelengths), then the reflection and the source will be out of phase, and the result will be darkness. So, by adding the light sent out to the reflected light which comes back we can tell how far the reflector on the target has moved. There are very accurate ways of doing this.

Laser measurement

The standard unit of length – the metre – can now be accurately reproduced using lasers. It is defined as the length of the path travelled by light in a vacuum in

$$\frac{1}{299\,792\,458}$$

of a second. The light used comes from a laser which uses a mixture of helium and neon gases. The NPL can reproduce the defined length of 1 metre to an accuracy of about 3 parts in 10^{11} – this is equivalent to measuring the circumference of the earth to the nearest millimetre! Thus, a very accurate measurement of one metre has been achieved.

Measuring the transmission properties of optical fibres.

One particularly useful way of measuring very small distances with lasers involves the principle of interference. When two light waves coincide they add together. If they are in phase then the result is brightness; if they are exactly out of phase they will cancel out and the result is darkness.

Since the light travels to the target and back, the target only moves by 1/4 of a wavelength between light and dark additions (fringes). The wavelength of visible light is about 600nm (1 nanometre = 1×10^{-9} m), so, by using the interference of laser light, and sub-dividing fringes, distances as small as 0.15 nm can be measured. This principle of measurement is called interferometry and research carried out by the NPL now enables the flatness of a mirror surface to be measured to the nearest 2 nm (2×10^{-9} m); about 40 times the radius of a hydrogen atom.

Measuring such small distances is very important to the manufacturers of microchips. One advantage of using lasers is that the measuring device does not touch what is being measured; light is merely bounced off it. Large telescopes need very accurately curved and smooth surfaces to prevent the image becoming distorted, so lasers are used to measure the smoothness because they can be used to measure very small changes in dimensions.

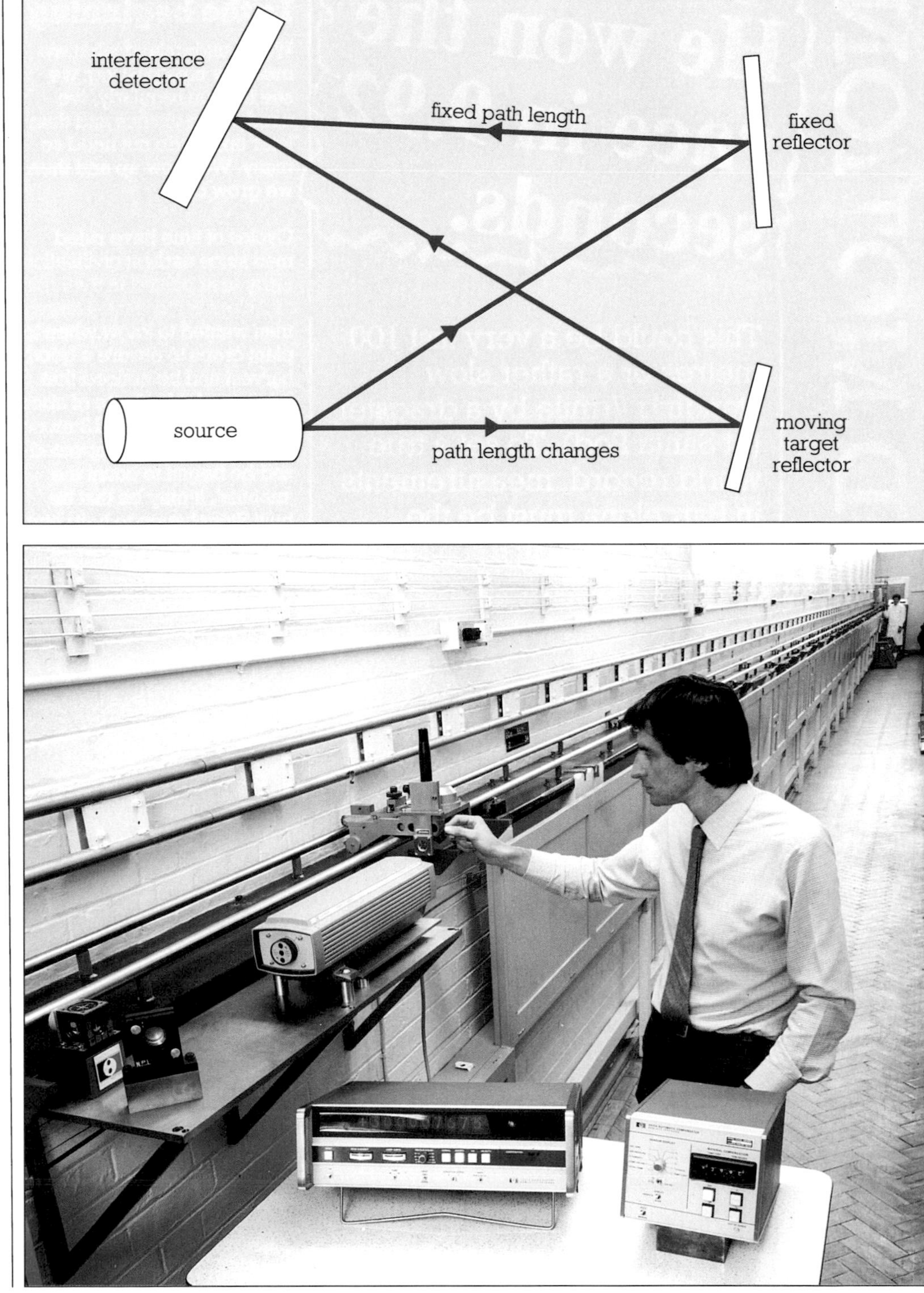

(Right) A 30 metre laser interferometer calibration facility at the NPL.

(Below) A high precision length measuring system.

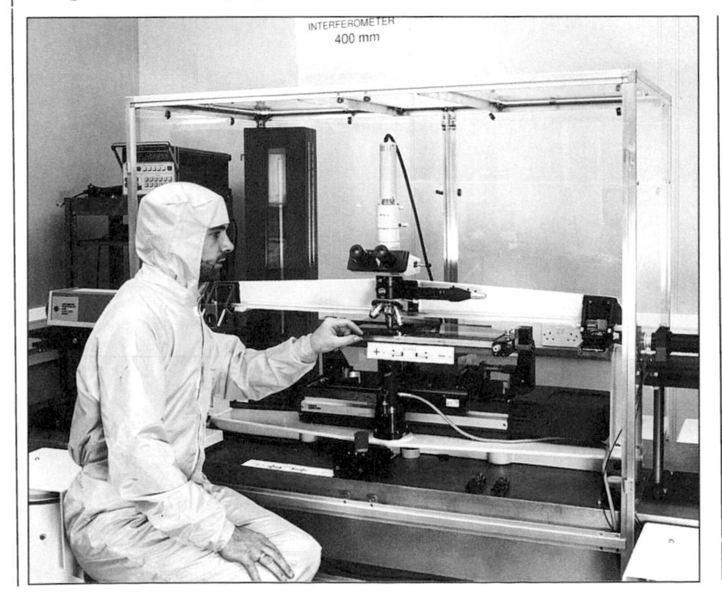

The James Clerk-Maxwell telescope in Hawaii, which has been measured by NPL using photogrammetric techniques.

4: TIME AND MOTION

He won the race in 9.92 seconds.

This could be a very fast 100 metres or a rather slow standing 1/4 mile by a dragster (at Santa Pod). To set a true world record, measurements in Barcelona must be the same as in Seoul and we must all measure distance and time to the same standards; the National Physical Laboratory keeps the UK standards which enable us to make international comparisons. Our ideas about time have changed over the years and so have the standards we use to measure it.

In the beginning

We all understand what we mean by time passing: we see the sun regularly, we need warm clothes and then, later on, we do not need so many. We grow up and then we grow old.

Cycles of time have ruled man since earliest civilisation. Early man hunted in the light and slept in the dark. Later, man wanted to know when to plant crops to ensure a good harvest and he noticed that the moon had a cycle of about 28 days. After about 13 moon cycles the seasons repeated and he began to count the 'months'. It may be that he built Stonehenge to help him keep count. To divide the day into shorter, more convenient, periods the sundial was used but these are not portable and certainly no use at night. But they do make very good clocks.

ACTIVITY

1. Take a straw, and some plasticine and a sheet of paper and construct a sundial. Observe how the position of the shadow moves round.
2. How can you calibrate your sundial without using a clock? Explain why your 'dial' is different from an ordinary clock dial.

To tell the time at night we can use a marked candle. How would you calibrate this? First you would make a batch of identical candles and take two of them. Then, light one of them next to your sundial and as this 'wasted' candle burns in the sunshine mark the unburnt candle with the hours as indicated by the sundial.

Using a sand glass was an easy way to measure the passing of time before clocks were invented.

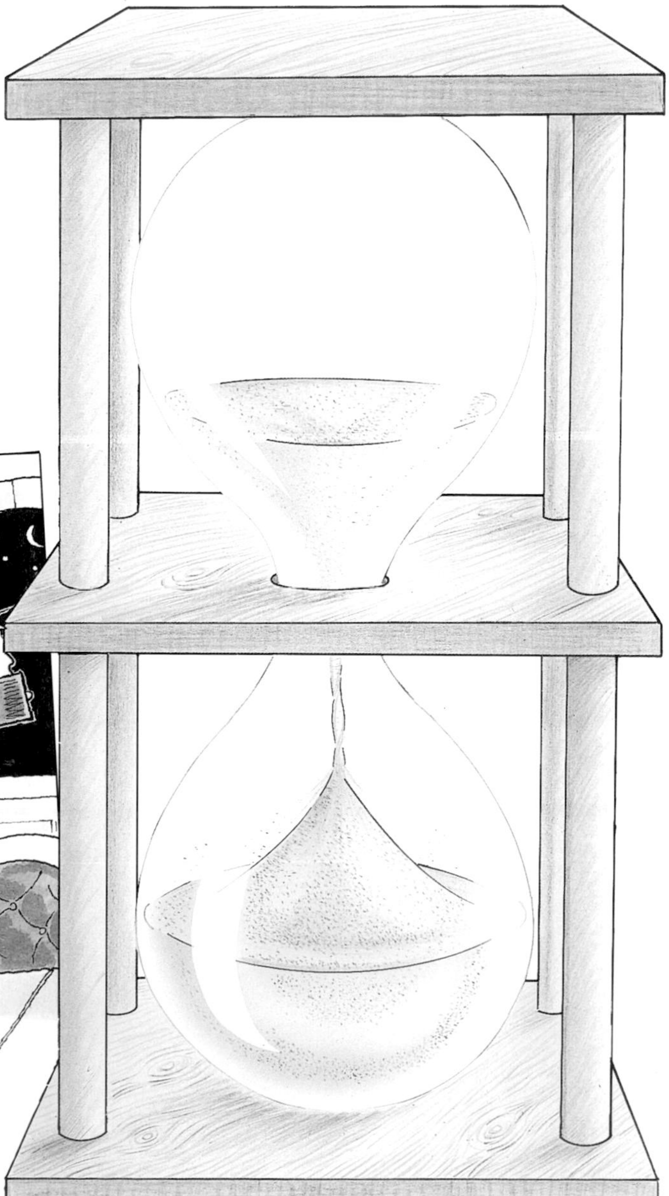

For more accurate measurement a mechanical device was needed. The idea of using the pendulum was developed by a number of famous scientists including Leonardo da Vinci, Galileo and Christian Huygens. Galileo might have recognised the regular swing of the pendulum by comparing it with his pulse. In a clock the regular swing of the pendulum moves a toothed wheel and a system of levers turns the hands; the swing is maintained by a coiled spring which needs winding.

A very accurate pendulum clock installed at the Royal Greenwich Observatory in 1925 showed that the period of the earth's rotation varied by up to 0.003 seconds each day. We now know that the earth's rotation round the sun varies by about one second per year, so the motion of the earth is of no use as a precise timekeeper.

(Right) The Great Clock of the Royal Exchange.

(Below) The NPL caesium clock.

How quickly time passes

As different days have different lengths physicists had to find something which absolutely never changed in order to make definitive time measurements. The answer was the humble caesium atom.

How does the caesium clock work? When you hit a tuning fork it vibrates at a definite frequency determined by its shape and the material it is made from. So does the caesium atom. When electrical energy is used to make it vibrate it sends out an electromagnetic wave of a very precise frequency. The second is defined as the time taken for 9 192 631 770 vibrations of the caesium atom. The only difficulty then, of course, is counting them! The NPL has devised a clock which uses the vibrating caesium atom to measure time and it supplies this time for the 'pips' on the radio, BT's Timeline and it also helps keep Big Ben on time.

Using time

Our ideas about distance have changed too, but to build a bridge over a river the bridge must be larger than the width of the river – easy with small rivers! But suppose the river is 1.5 km wide. To measure large distances accurately we use lasers or radar which are both types of electromagnetic radiation.

We know very accurately how fast this radiation travels in air. If we reflect a pulse of radar waves from an object on the far side of the river and measure how long the pulse takes to travel to the far side and back, we can calculate how far away the object is. So we are using a time measurement in order to measure distance.

ACTIVITY

Astronauts left a mirror on the moon. Scientists have shone a powerful laser at the mirror and measured the time taken for the pulse to travel there and back as 2.5 seconds. Light travels at 3.0×10^8 ms^{-1}. How far away is the moon?
[Distance = speed × time]

This is exactly how a radio altimeter works in an aeroplane. By sending out radar pulses and measuring the time they take to bounce back from the ground the instrument can calculate the aircraft's altitude. Ships use sound waves in the same way to find the depth below the keel – this is called sonar.

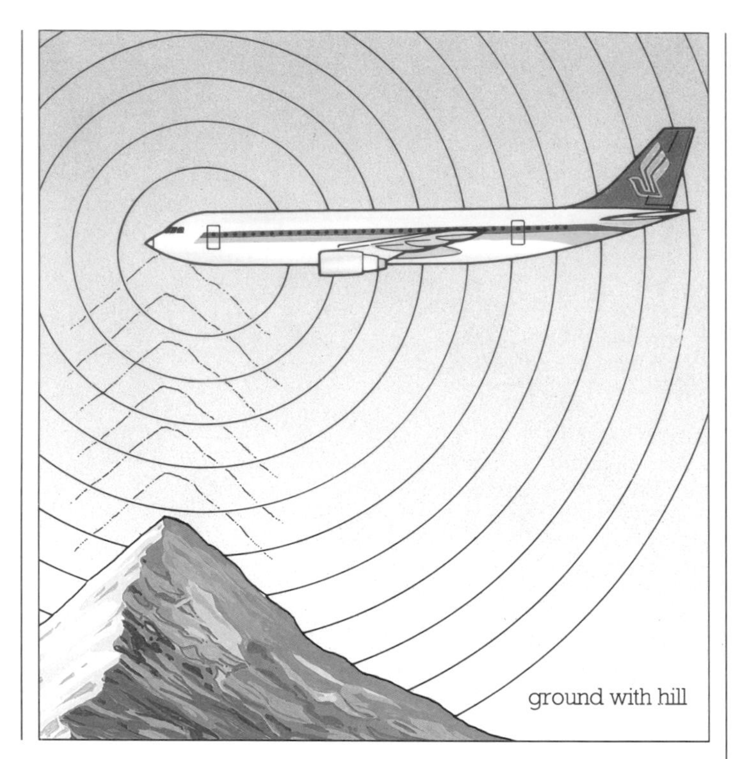

Observer hears siren as lower notes

Doppler shift (Standard Doppler wave pattern)

By measuring the frequency change of a signal we can measure the speed of an object by bouncing waves off it.

When you stand in the street and a fire engine passes it often sounds its siren. As the fire engine approaches the siren sounds higher in pitch (or frequency). As it goes away from you the siren sounds lower in frequency. This is the Doppler shift. Coming towards you the waves are bunched up and the vibrations hit your ear more often – the frequency is higher. Going away the vibrations hit your ear less often so the frequency is lower The siren is sending out the same frequency all the time.

We know that sound travels at about 330 ms^{-1} in air at sea level, so by measuring the change in frequency we can calculate the speed of the train – it might be 40 ms^{-1} or $1/8$ the speed of sound. The Doppler shift is also observed with electromagnetic waves like light. We do not observe this effect in everyday life because light travels at 300 000 km s^{-1} and not even a Jaguar winning at Le Mans travels at $1/8$ of this speed. If we bounce radar waves off a Jaguar car the Doppler shift is very small since it travels slowly with respect to the speed of light, but the reflected radar waves are still shifted. By comparing the reflected frequency with the transmitted frequency we can calculate the speed of the car. Since we can measure time – or frequency – very accurately we can measure the speed of the Jaguar. This is of interest to the race officials at Le Mans, or even the motorway police!

In aircraft the instruments can tell how fast the plane is travelling in the same way. A radar beacon transmits a particular frequency, and because the plane is moving it will receive a Doppler shifted frequency. By measuring the amount of shift the instruments calculate the speed of the plane over the ground. The instrument landing system (ILS) thus knows how high the aircraft is and how fast it is going and in which direction, and the ILS can actually land the aircraft even if the pilot cannot see through the windscreen. But of course bats have been doing this for years – they use sound not radar!

Often human beings can tell the direction of a sound – close your eyes and try it! You might find it more difficult than you expect.

The ear nearest the source of the sound registers the sound slightly before the ear on the other side of your head. Your on-board computer, or brain, detects this small difference in time, perhaps only a few microseconds, and points you in the right direction.

A wavefront is formed by sound radiating out in a circle from the siren. The siren is in the centre of wavefronts i, ii, iii and iv.

Wavefront i was produced when the siren was in position 1. It is a circle with its centre at position 1. The same goes for wavefronts ii, iii and iv but, because the siren is moving each wavefront has a different centre. This means that as the centre of the circle (the siren) moves to the right, the wavelength is smaller on the right than on the left. Someone at point A would therefore hear higher notes than someone at point B.

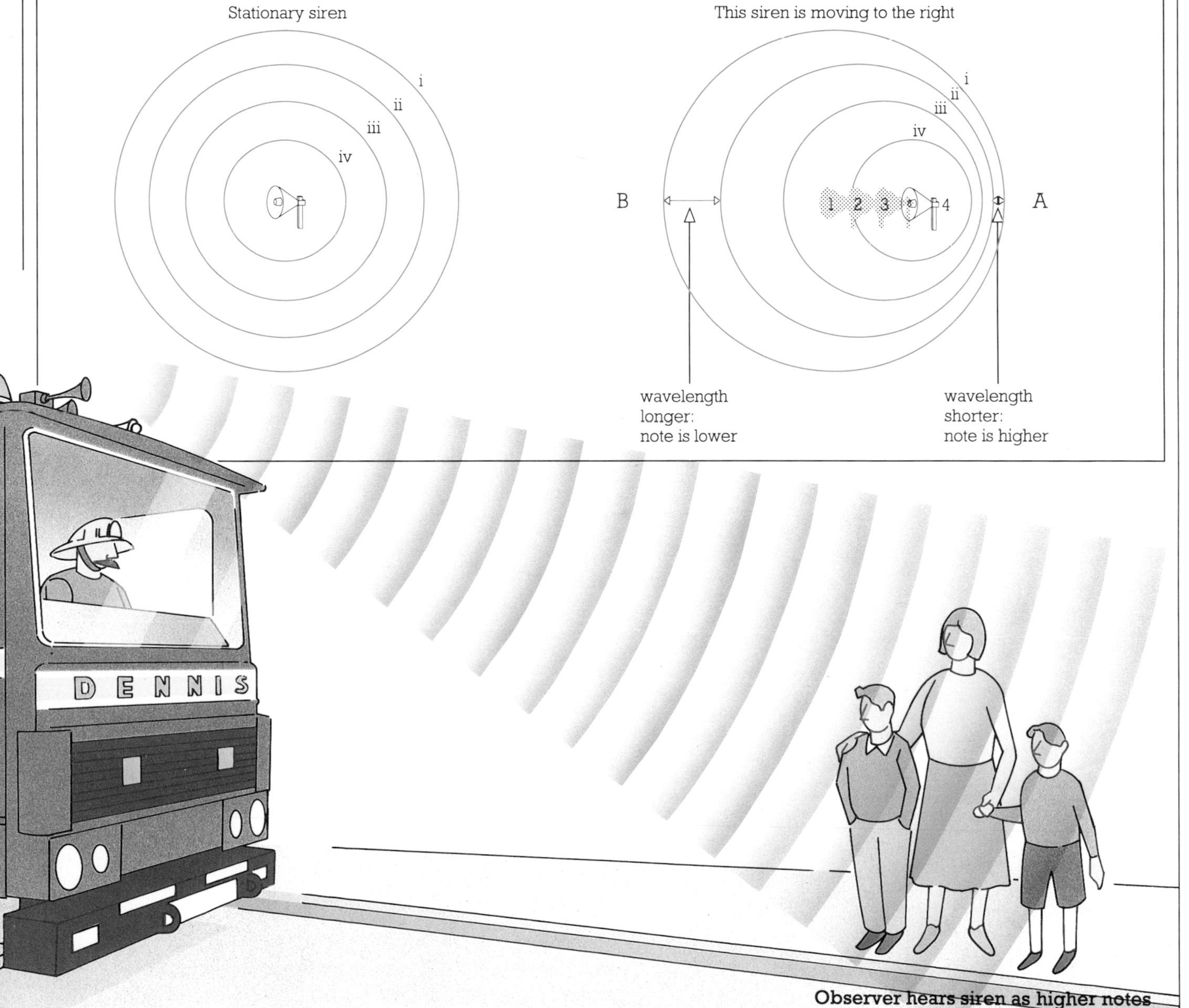

5: MEASUREMENT IN MEDICINE

We are measured from the cradle to the grave. Weight and length are recorded when we are born and, finally, when we are measured for our coffins. A huge number of different measurements are made as we move through life. Many of these are simply to find what size clothes we need or to check that progress is normal – height and weight should be related as we grow up. The National Curriculum is designed to monitor, or measure, our intellectual development. Some measurements are much more precise and can be a matter of life or death. Accurate readings and measurements are vital for diagnosis and the monitoring of body functions in medicine.

The human body is a sensitive organism but still highly resilient to all that the outside world can throw at it. Broken bones will join together when set in the correct position; cuts in the skin are cleansed and disinfected before the skin joins together again; viruses and bacteria which invade the body are fought by the immune system. When we fall ill or are injured our bodies devote much of their resources to repairing the damage or fighting the illness; we may lose our energy and feel tired, and our body temperature may rise. By measuring temperature, pulse rate and blood pressure, doctors can often make diagnoses very quickly. Many illnesses require more complex measurements and doctors use a wide range of accurate and calibrated monitoring instruments in order to check the progress of a patient when recovering from serious illness or injury. How does the complex organism work normally?

Intensive care.

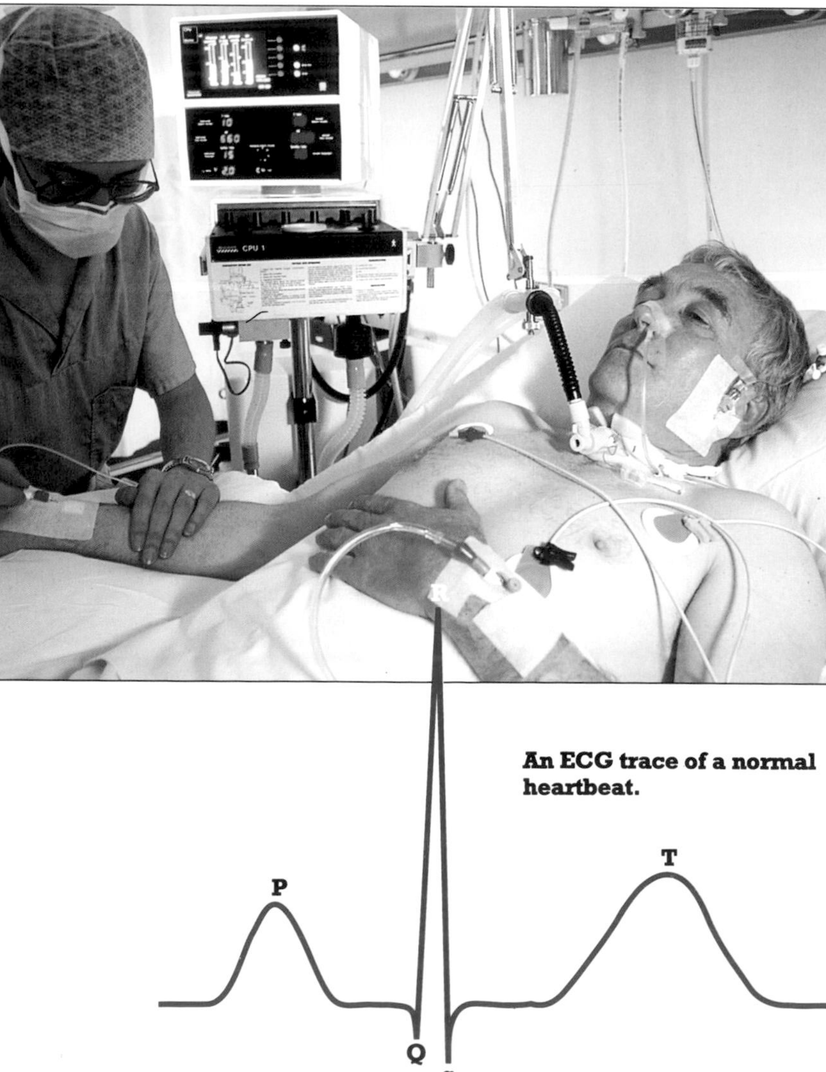

An ECG trace of a normal heartbeat.

P
R
Q
S
T

Measuring heartbeats

In order to make the heart contract, chemical changes occur which produce an electrical charge across the heart. This electrical signal can be picked up by sensitive electrodes placed on the skin – a remote measurement which can be displayed on a cathode ray oscilloscope after being amplified. The device which does this is called an electrocardiogram, or ECG. In practice, the electrical signal is complex and the regularity and height of the peaks and the troughs indicate what the heart is doing. A large peak represents the contraction of the ventricles. When an ECG is different from a normal one, experienced doctors can make detailed diagnoses on the unhealthy heart.

If the ECG is not normal, it might be that the heart has lost its sensitivity to the electrical impulses or that the impulses themselves are too weak. One solution is to fit a pacemaker. This is an electronic device which can be connected to the heart directly; it produces regular, strong electrical pulses which stimulate the heart to contract and ensure an even circulation of blood. One problem with these is that they 'beat' constantly and so the heart rate is 70 per minute whether you are asleep in bed or running for the bus. However, recent experiments with acidity sensors are showing that the next generation of pacemakers will be able to function more like a normal heart and change their pace according to the CO_2 concentration in the blood.

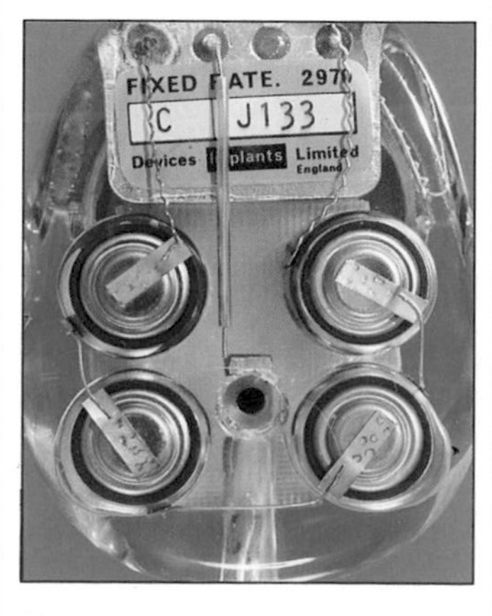

An old fashioned external pacemaker.

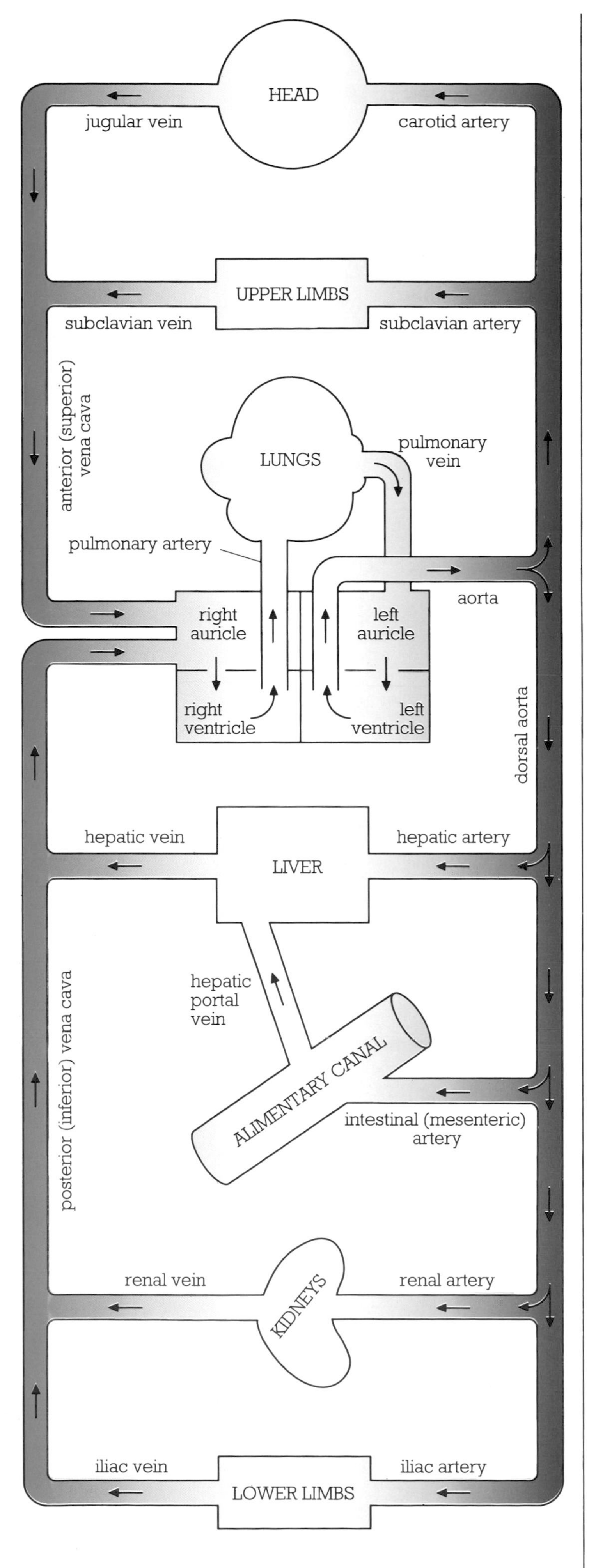

A diagrammatic model of the human circulatory system.

Blood pressure

In order to pass a liquid through a pipe it must be put under pressure – this is the function of the heart. If either the pump or the pipes become unserviceable then the circulation slows down, cells do not get fed properly and muscles run down. One main cause of circulation problems is the build up of fatty tissue in the blood vessels and around the heart – these are most likely to be caused by high intakes of cholesterol. Measuring blood pressure is another common way of monitoring the health of a person's heart. If fatty deposits block the arteries then the heart has to work harder to pump blood, and the increased pressure can cause damage to the heart.

Just like a central heating system, the blood will not circulate very well through pipes which have become 'furred up'.

How do we measure pressure? In order to make a liquid rise up a straw you can either create a lower pressure at the top – sucking – or a greater pressure at the bottom – blowing. The only way to drink a can of coke with a straw is by sucking but blood pressure is measured by how far mercury can be made to rise up a tube by the pressure needed to cut off the blood supply. A cuff is placed around the upper arm and inflated with a pump, and by listening to the artery with a stethoscope a nurse can measure the pressure applied through the cuff which just stops the pulse. As the nurse gradually reduces the pressure the blood starts to flow again, but then the pulse in the stethoscope becomes quieter suddenly and the pressure is read again. Thus we have two pressure readings, say, '120 over 80'.

The first figure is the height of the mercury column when the blood supply is just cut off – this is the systolic pressure and corresponds to the maximum pressure produced by the ventricle. The second figure is the diastolic pressure and corresponds to the pressure when the heart is relaxed – this is the more significant figure.

An organ such as the heart is reasonably easily monitored, and the measurements made are a good guide to the general health of a patient.

Blood pressure is a measurement of the pressure that blood exerts against the walls of the main arteries and is quoted in millimetres of mercury.

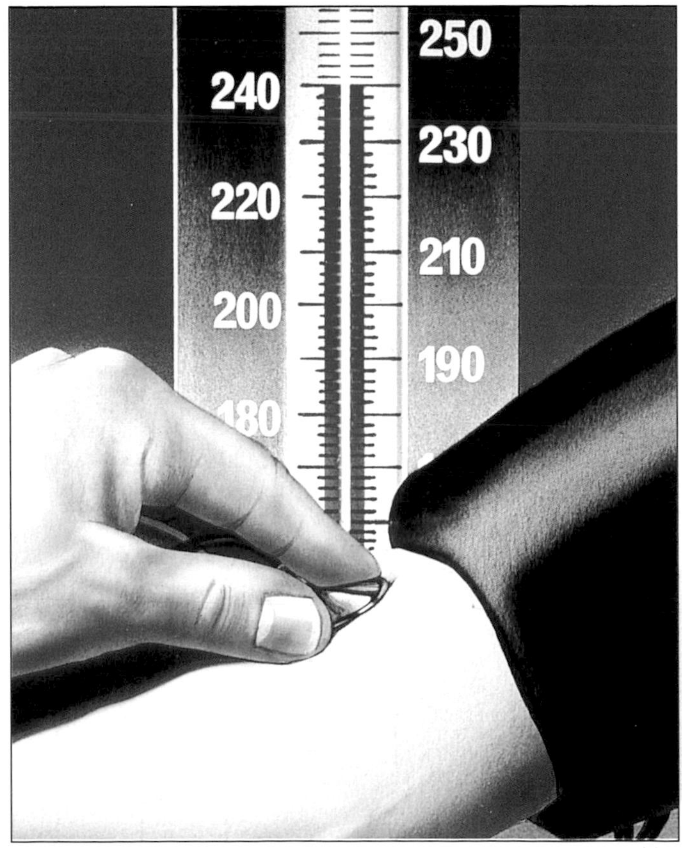

Ultrasound

During pregnancy a direct image of the growing baby may be made by using modern scanner techniques in order to measure and monitor its development. How is it done?

Radar works by emitting a pulse of electromagnetic waves which bounce off the target, and the reflection is picked up near the source (see chapter 4). This is fine for long distances, but for short distances the time between the transmission of the pulse and the reception of the reflection is too short to be easily used. Sound travels very much slower, about 330 ms^{-1} in air (at sea level), and is easily used for small distances since the time delay is now long enough to be easily measured. Submarines use sound waves in sonar in order to find things underwater, so do dolphins. Bats use a high frequency sound to detect flying insects (food) and obstacles.

Ultrasound is also used in medicine. As the name suggests it is a very high frequency sound, which means that the human ear cannot detect it – see Table 1.

Sound waves at this frequency travel easily through the baby and are partially reflected by parts of it. When reflected by a moving part – for example blood – the reflection is Doppler shifted (see chapter 4) and images may be built up with the aid of computers. Thus, images of unseen objects, such as the beating of an unborn baby's heart, may be assembled.

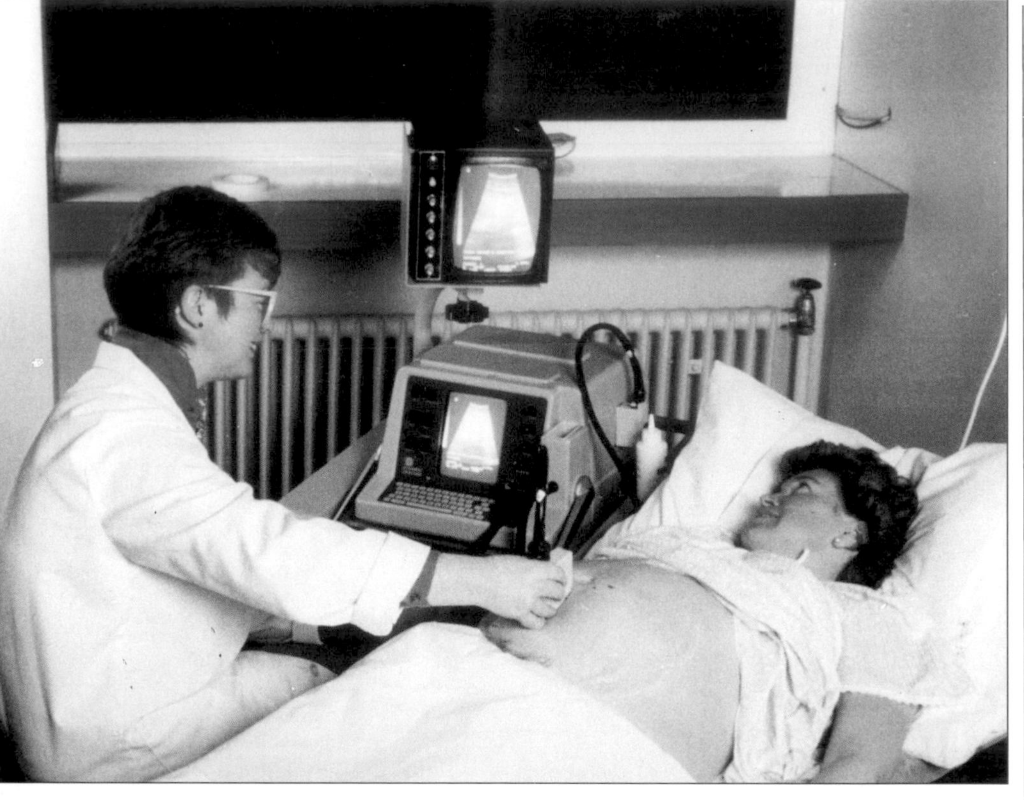

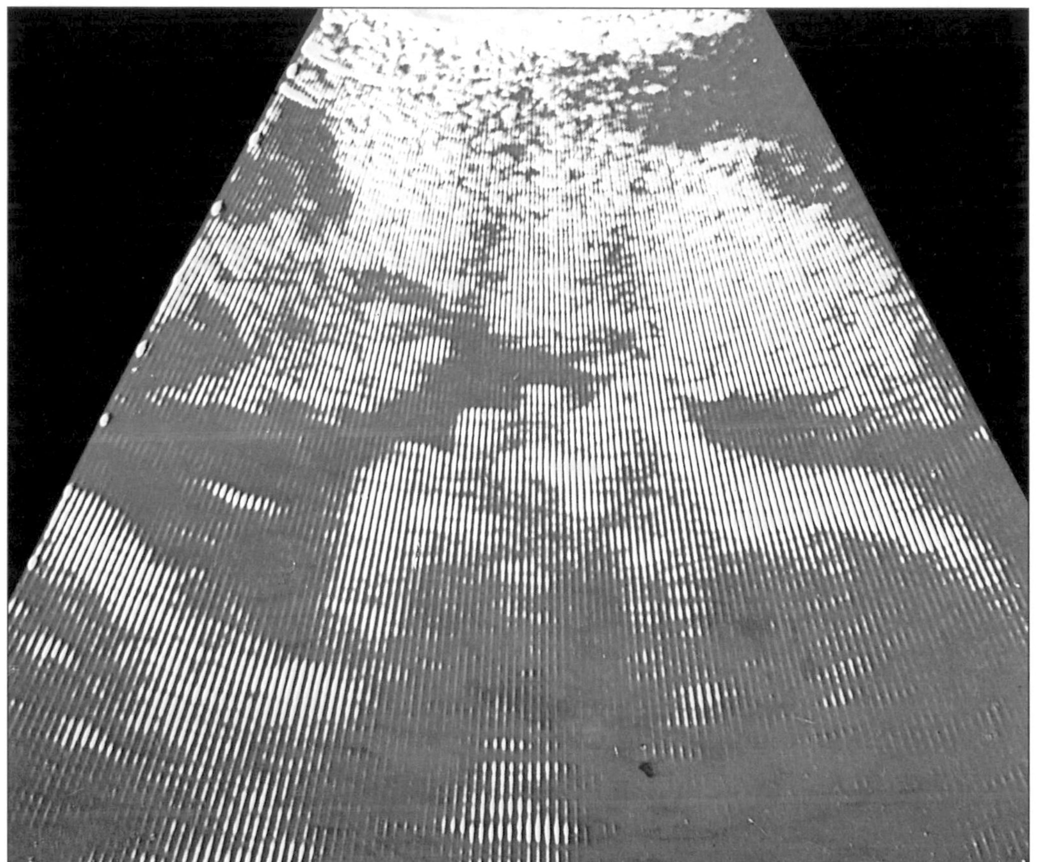

(Top) A pregnant woman having an ultrasound scan.

(Right) A photograph of an actual scan.

Table 1

SOUND		
Human ear	20 Hz — 20 kHz	(2×10^4 Hz)
Dolphins	30 kHz — 50 kHz	(5×10^4 Hz)
Ultrasound	1 MHz — 10 MHz	(1×10^7 Hz)
Electromagnetic		
VHF radio	100 MHz	(1×10^8 Hz)
Visible light	5×10^{14} Hz	
Radar	10^{18} Hz	
X-rays	10^{19} Hz	

X-rays

When these were first discovered by Röntgen in 1895 he realised that they were rays, ie they travelled in straight lines, but he did not know whether they were wave trains like light or streams of particles, so he called them X (the unknown factor) rays. We now know that they are electromagnetic rays, like light but with a much higher frequency (see the diagram on page 16).

At this frequency it is easier to think of them as particles of energy travelling in straight lines. In fact, the X-ray band covers quite a wide range of frequencies and they are useful for diagnosis – finding out what's wrong – and for therapy – putting it right.

Diagnosis

X-rays have sufficient energy to cause some chemical reactions to occur. When a piece of paper covered with suitable chemicals (or film) is hit by X-rays then a reaction takes place and when the film is developed dark patches show up where the X-rays hit. This is just like an ordinary camera film except that in a camera visible light produces the chemical change.

The human body is made up of different structures. Some of them, such as bones, will absorb X-rays, whilst others, such as the liver, allow most of the X-rays through. The body is composed mostly of water which lets X-rays pass through completely unhindered. To make a 'hidden' measurement, such as a check on a broken arm bone, it is a simple matter to place the arm in front of a piece of X-ray film and 'shine' X-rays through the arm. Where the X-rays pass through, the film goes dark (when developed) and where the bone is in the way the film remains light. Hence we can see a picture of broken bones.

By adjusting the accelerating voltage we can vary the frequency of the X-rays. A high frequency X-ray will pass through, almost anything – even metal – but a low frequency X-ray is stopped by even flimsy material. So, by varying the voltage, we can adjust the 'hardness' of the X-rays and we can either take X-ray pictures of bones or of softer tissues, such as a liver or kidney. In fact, pictures may be taken of thick welds in oil-rig structures to see if there are any defects. This is an example of non-destructive testing.

X-ray therapy

X-rays have been widely used in the treatment of cancer, as have other forms of radiotherapy. The basic principle is that the radiation they produce is a type of energy, and by focusing this energy onto tumours they can be destroyed. Great care must be taken with the penetrating power (or frequency) and the amounts of radiation delivered in order to minimise the damage to normal, healthy tissue. Measuring radiation dosage to achieve the optimum result is called dosemetry and standards of dosemetry are set by the National Physical Laboratory. To check an X-ray machine the radiologist radiates a dosemeter which is then posted to the NPL which will then determine the dose that has actually been administered.

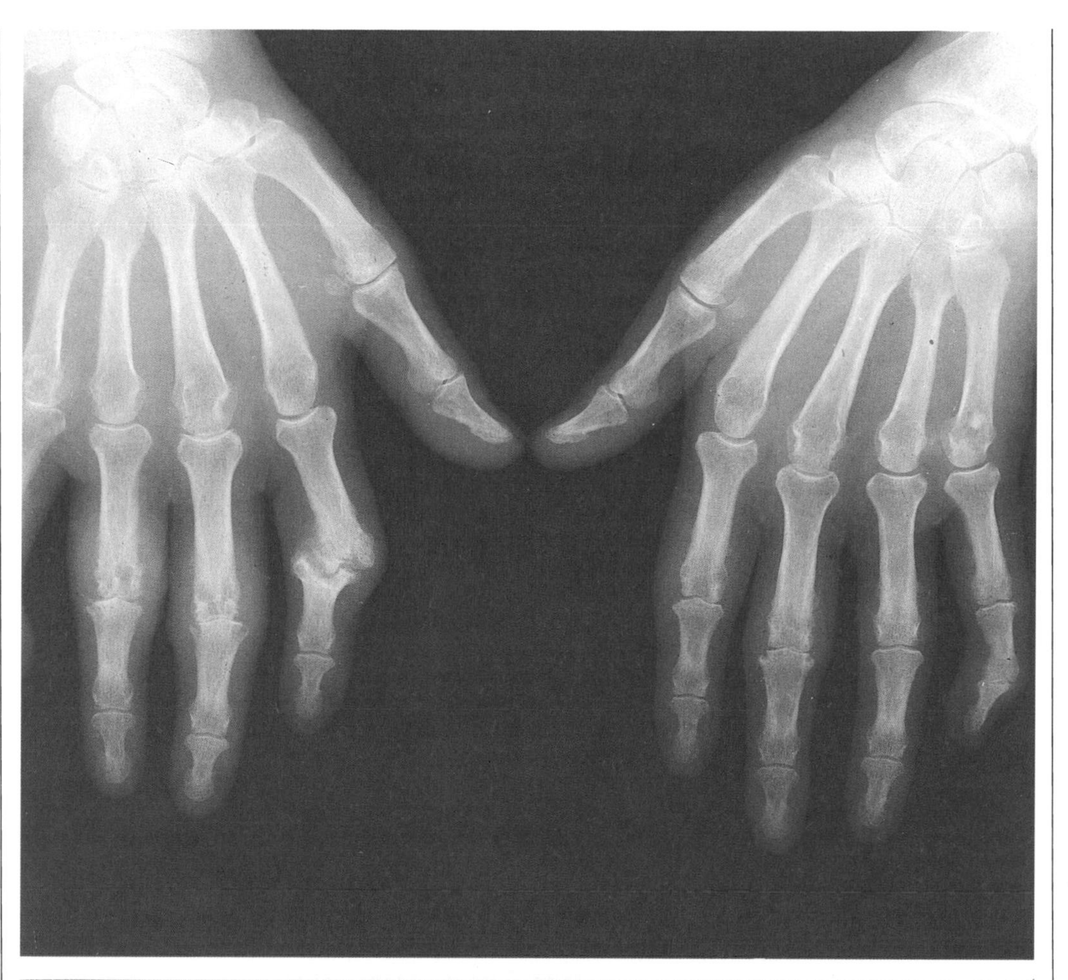

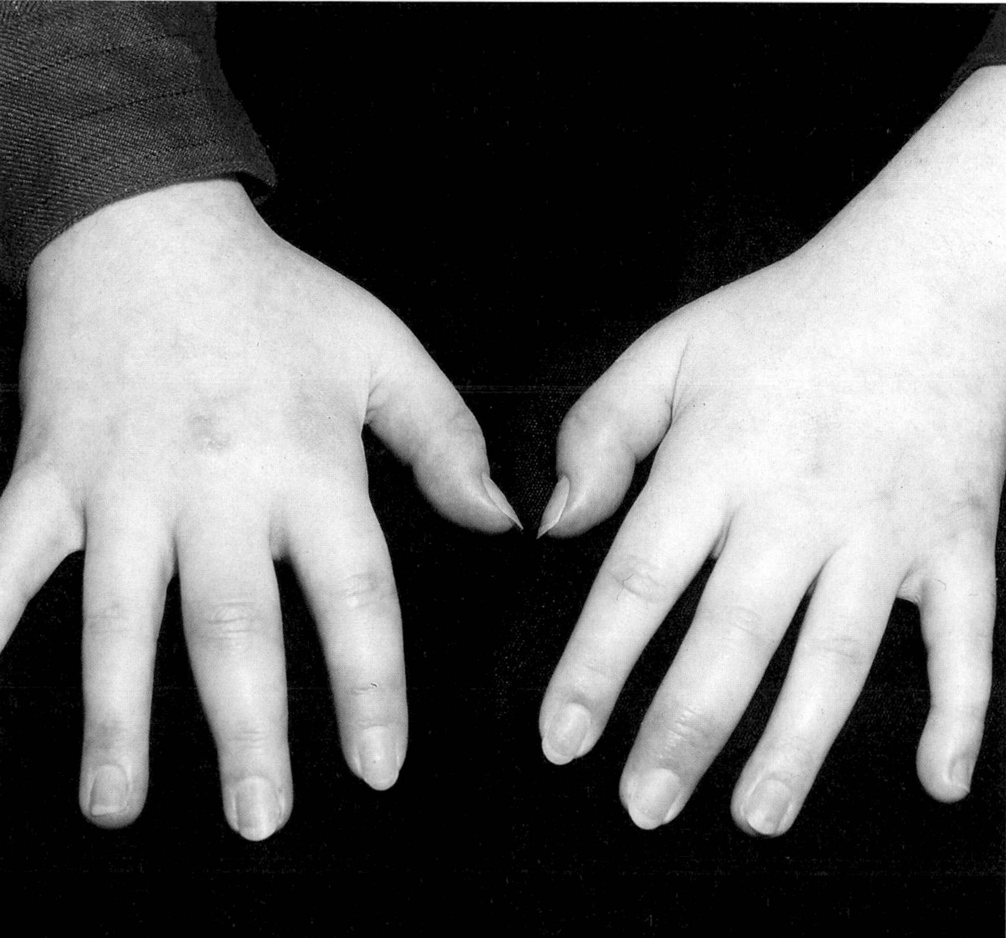

(Top) An X-ray of arthritic hands shows the reasons for the misshapen and swollen fingers.

Ionising radiation

Radiation with much more energy than X-rays is produced when the nucleus of an atom is disturbed. Some of these disturbances occur naturally when atoms change spontaneously and emit radiation, and more usable energy is available when atoms are made to split – this is the basis of nuclear power. Radioactivity measurements are of vital importance in nuclear power plants in order to keep the reactor safe and to protect the workers from damage. A valuable spin-off from the research into nuclear power has been the medical uses to which radioactivity can be put.

What is radioactivity?

The atom consists of protons, neutrons and electrons. The nucleus is where the protons and neutrons are found, and the electrons orbit at various distances around it – rather like the planets orbit the Sun in our solar system.

A nuclide is a type of nucleus with a specific number of protons and neutrons; the number of protons determines which chemical element it is. The isotopes of an element are two nuclides with the same number of protons – hence the same chemical – but different numbers of neutrons. Carbon-12 has six neutrons and carbon-14 has eight neutrons; since they are both carbon they both have six protons. So, the final number refers to the number of nucleons – that is protons plus neutrons. Carbon -14 is naturally radioactive, which means that it decays by emitting β-particles. Other atoms emit a variety of particles.

α - particles consist of 2 protons and 2 neutrons – a helium nucleus
β - particles are high speed electrons
γ - rays are very short, very localised pulses of electromagnetic radiation with a much higher frequency than X-rays.

These particles are all emitted from the nucleus of an atom when that atom undergoes a change in its nucleus. They are emitted at very high speed and when they encounter an ordinary atom they knock electrons off the atom, leaving it as a positively charged ion – hence the name ionising radiation.

Nuclear power uses the property that very large atoms can be made unstable so that they split into two parts and each part of the nucleus becomes reduced to a different element. Naturally occurring radioactivity usually involves a small change and the emission of a single particle. One fuel for a nuclear reactor is uranium-235, and when this absorbs a neutron it becomes unstable and breaks into two parts, such as strontium-90 and caesium-137. The problem with nuclear power is that these products of the split are themselves radioactive – they will not split, but they give off ionising radiation and are consequently still dangerous to living things. It is the disposal of this nuclear waste which causes medical and environmental problems. We shall consider radiations produced by spontaneously decaying nuclides, such as cobalt-60 which emits γ-radiation.

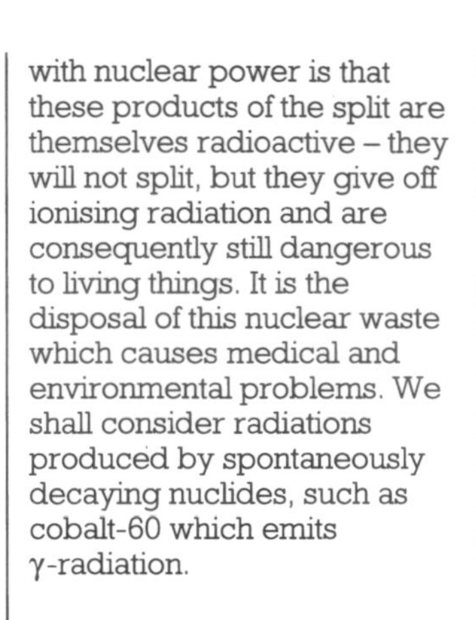

How radioactivity is measured

Electric current is a flow of electrons. When an ionising particle moves through a gas it leaves a trail of positive ions and separated electrons. By persuading the electrons to move and be collected we have an electric current which can be measured by normal measuring devices.

Although these radiations affect photographic paper, just like X-rays, the principal instrument for detecting radiation is the Geiger-Müller tube (GM tube), much loved in science fiction films. The GM tube works on the principle of collecting the electrons knocked off by the radiation.

Unfortunately they don't 'click' as in the films, unless they are fitted with a loudspeaker. A GM tube is a cylinder with a spike down the middle and a very thin window at one end. The case is kept at zero volts – or earth potential – and the spike has a positive potential of a few hundred volts. When the radiation enters through the thin window it produces electrons by colliding with the gas atoms in the tube.

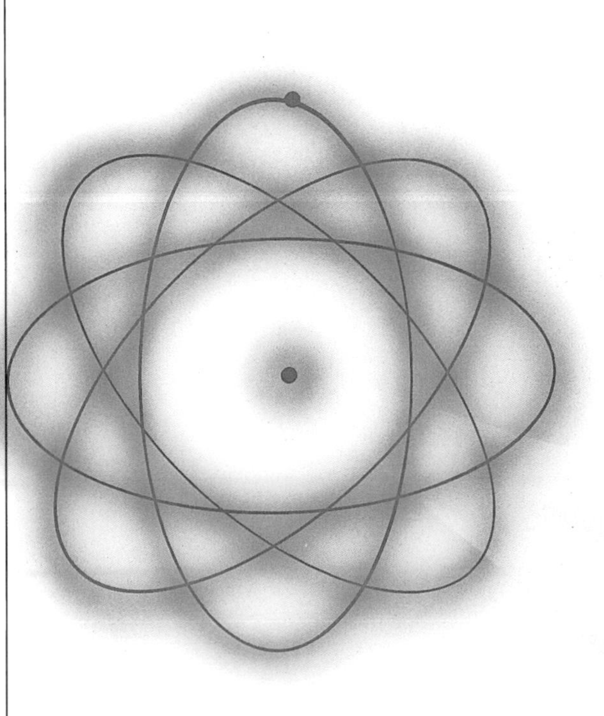

The structure of an atom.

The negative electrons are strongly attracted to the positive spike and produce more ions and electrons themselves. Thus an avalanche of electrons arrives at the spike and this, in effect, produces a very small pulse of current. The positive ions are repelled by the spike and drift relatively slowly to the side of the tube. The pulse of the current is amplified electronically and the larger pulse is used for counting – this is also done electronically in modern equipment.

How is radiation kept safely?

When the radiation produces ions it loses energy. A γ-ray then ceases to exist but the α and β particles simply slow down a little. If enough ionisations are made the particle moves so slowly that it cannot ionise any more – it is no longer ionising radiation and we say it has been absorbed.

An α-particle produces a lot of ions in a short distance since it is so big (relative to the others) and so it runs out of energy very quickly. It therefore has a short range, typically 1 cm in air, and it is stopped by a sheet of paper. A β-particle produces fewer ions but has a longer range – typically 25 cm in air – and it will penetrate 2-3 mm of aluminium before being absorbed. It is, however, stopped by lead.

γ-radiation has no charge and no mass – it is 'pure energy'. It produces few ions, but because it is most penetrating, it is the most dangerous. It is never fully absorbed – even by several centimetres of lead.

To keep a radioactive source safely we must keep it a long way from living things and surround it with a shield of a dense substance such as lead. Thus the shield absorbs much of the radiation, but any which gets through has less chance of hitting us if we are far away, since its direction is random.

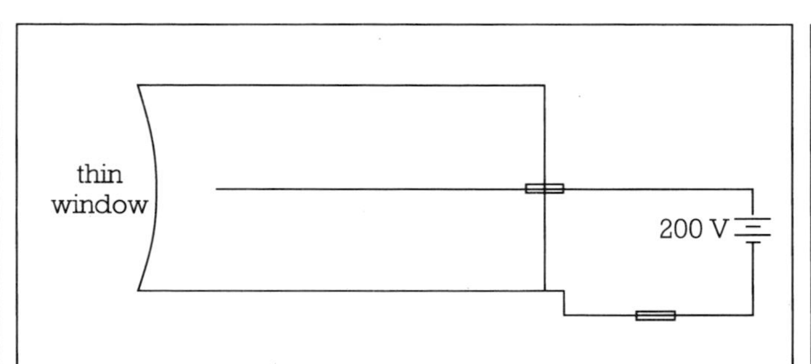

(Top) Diagram of a Geiger-Müller tube.

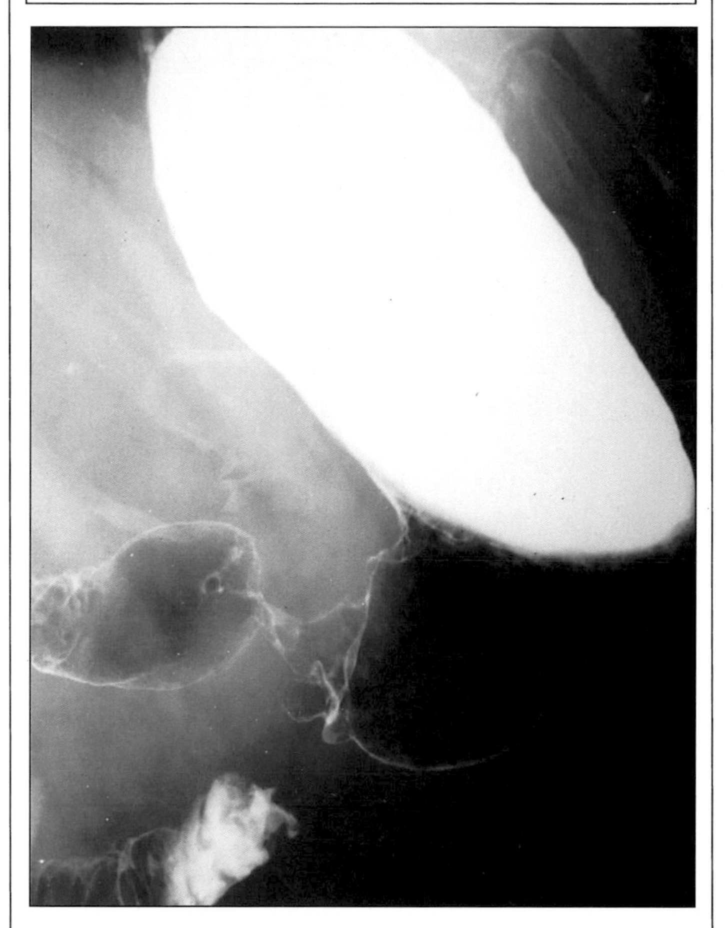

(Middle) False-colour barium meal X-ray showing the stomach.

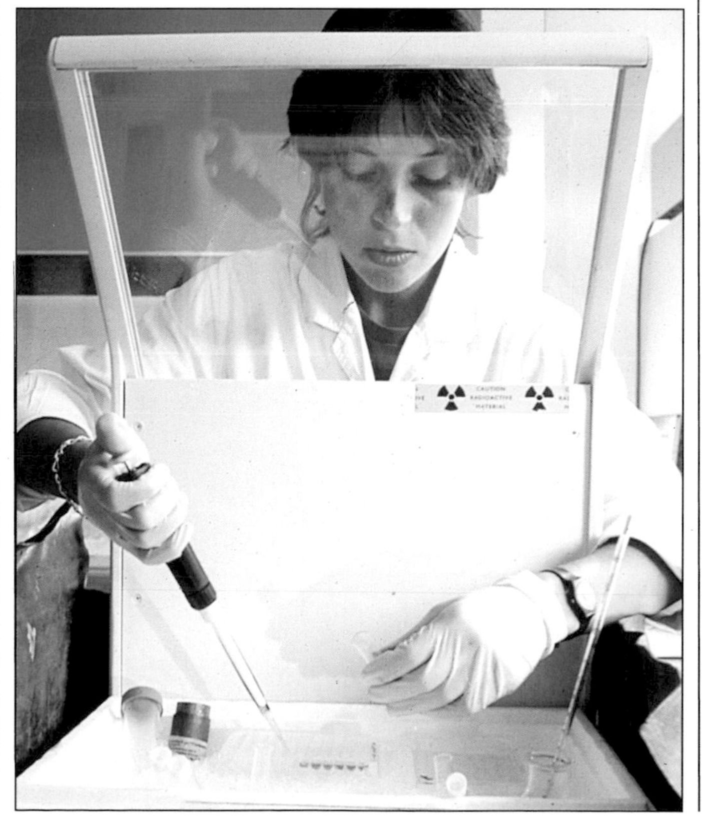

Radioactive labelling in immunological research. The scientist observes necessary and stringent safety precautions.

How radiation is useful

Malignant growths inside the body might be too difficult to cut out because they are too close to vital organs. By finding out the exact location of the growth using X-rays we can bombard the tumour with radiation and kill the malignant tissue without operating.

Minute doses of radiation are relatively harmless and the body soon recovers. Since radioactive decay is unaffected by the chemical combination of molecules (the particles come from the nucleus) we can use radioactive substances as tracers to discover what happens to chemicals in the body. Compounds can be manufactured using radioactive isotopes instead of the normal isotope and when these compounds are ingested by a human being we can trace exactly how the chemical moves through the body. This enables doctors to diagnose which parts of the body are functioning properly and can help diagnose illnesses which are undetectable by other means. Doses must be accurately measured against NPL standards – too big a dose could harm the patient.

Anyone who works with radioactive substances has to observe stringent safety precautions. Various detectors are provided which monitor the specific type of radiation that is being used. Different types of radiation need different detectors. Normally, the detectors are checked every month to make sure that workers have not become exposed to too much radiation. If, however, an accident is suspected then the detector is checked immediately. Measurement of this exposure is of vital importance to these workers and the NPL maintains standards of radioactivity which are used to calibrate the measuring devices used in hospitals and in the nuclear power industry.

6: MEASURING THE ENVIRONMENT

We take the air we breathe for granted with every breath we take. The damage the air can do to us makes headline news every time there is a hurricane or snow-storm. More significantly, the damage we do to the environment is now the concern of everybody, whether they own a factory or an aerosol.

The weather has always been of interest, especially to the British, and advances in technology enable us to make more precise measurements over much wider areas. However, even modern supercomputers are unable to forecast exactly whether it will rain and for how long.

Measuring the environment is of less immediate interest, but advances in laser and space technology are giving us more direct measurements of pollution levels which help tell us how to limit the damage and to start to clean up the environment.

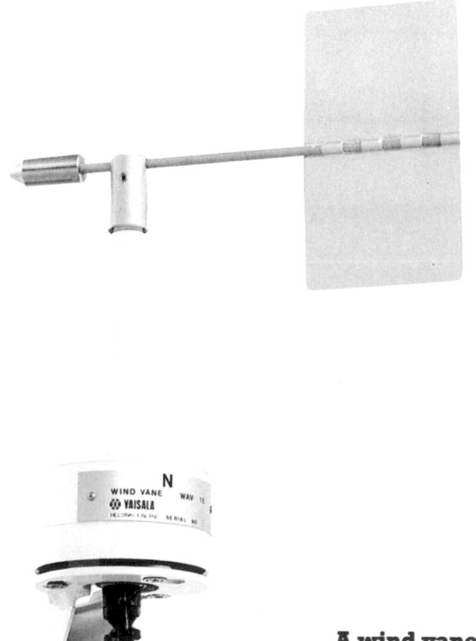

A wind vane.

Weather

Systems of weather are huge phenomena, but as observers we report on temperature, pressure, wind speed and direction and whether it is raining. It is much more difficult, however, to gather lots of observations together and produce an overall pattern.

Weather forecasters on TV show us satellite photographs taken only an hour before, yet only 100 years ago forecasting was largely a matter of studying past patterns and predicting which pattern would repeat itself next.

Today's sophisticated communication networks give us fast and accurate weather forecasts throughout the day.

Wind

Church spires often have early weather indicators on top – weather vanes – but these do not tell the observer much more than he can feel for himself. (It is difficult to measure wind speed as it is invisible, but we can measure the effect of the wind.) In 1846 the cup anemometer was invented and accurate measurements of wind speed could be made. Three or four hemispherical cups rotate about a vertical axis, and the speed of the cups indicates the force of the wind. The speed can be measured by a mechanical counter, but modern anemometers use electronics.

Before the anemometer, the force of the wind was judged by how much sail a ship could carry. Sailors were, of course, very interested in wind strength. Admiral Beaufort, who was a contemporary of Nelson, invented the scale by which wind strength is still judged.

Satellite picture of Hurricane Alicia.

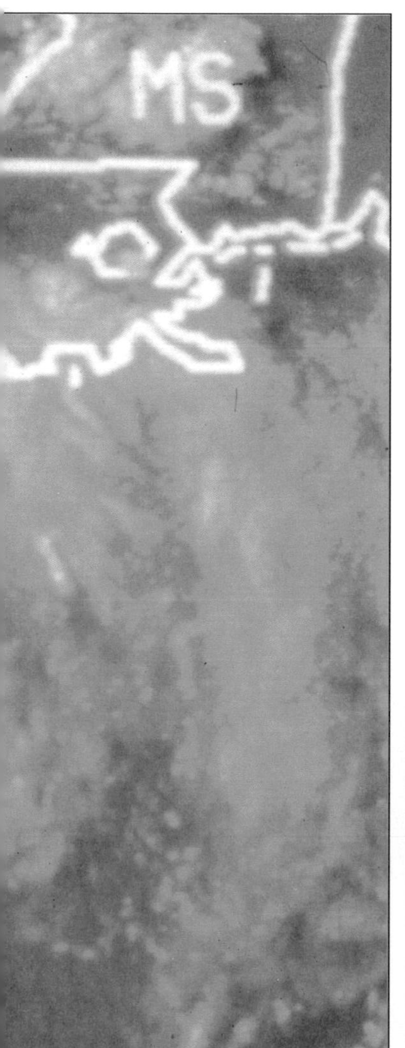

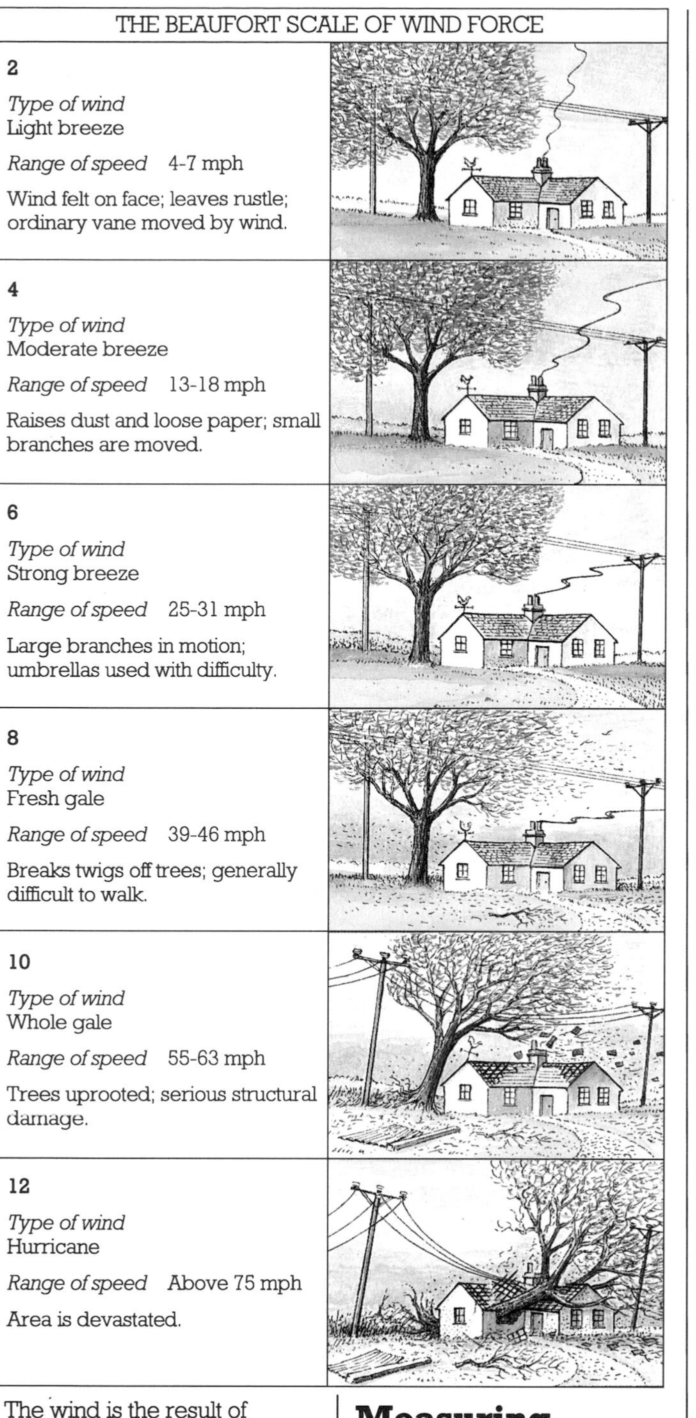

THE BEAUFORT SCALE OF WIND FORCE
2 *Type of wind* Light breeze *Range of speed* 4-7 mph Wind felt on face; leaves rustle; ordinary vane moved by wind.
4 *Type of wind* Moderate breeze *Range of speed* 13-18 mph Raises dust and loose paper; small branches are moved.
6 *Type of wind* Strong breeze *Range of speed* 25-31 mph Large branches in motion; umbrellas used with difficulty.
8 *Type of wind* Fresh gale *Range of speed* 39-46 mph Breaks twigs off trees; generally difficult to walk.
10 *Type of wind* Whole gale *Range of speed* 55-63 mph Trees uprooted; serious structural damage.
12 *Type of wind* Hurricane *Range of speed* Above 75 mph Area is devastated.

The wind is the result of differences in air pressure due to the movements of gigantic air masses moving as a result of the radiation from the sea and the Earth's rotation. There are more local effects which alter the wind pattern over only a few miles.

Measuring pressure

In the UK, low pressure usually means unsettled and rainy weather, and a mass of air at high pressure usually brings fine weather. Winds tend to circle around regions of low pressure in much the same way as bath water tends to swirl as it falls through the plug-hole. So to help predict the weather we must be able to measure pressure, and the most common device is called a barometer.

The National Physical Laboratory has been responsible for standards of pressure measurement since its foundation in 1900 and still calibrates barometers and ultra-high and ultra-low pressure gauges with ever increasing accuracy.

When you drink with a straw you are reducing the liquid pressure at the top with your mouth, and the pressure of the atmosphere on the surface of the liquid then forces the water up the straw. Suppose you had a very full straw; you need to suck harder to raise the liquid a certain distance than you would if the straw had been empty when you began to suck.

Is there a limit? If you could create a perfect vacuum at the top, how far would the water rise up? The answer is over 10 metres. To make a barometer we use mercury, a much denser liquid. If there is a perfect vacuum at the top the mercury will rise a much shorter distance since it is heavier. Atmospheric pressure varies from hour to hour but the standard of atmospheric pressure is the pressure which will push the mercury 760 mm up the tube. A unit of pressure can therefore be defined in mm of Hg. Another unit for pressure is the bar, and the standard atmosphere is 1.0132 bar or 1013.2 mbar (millibar or thousandths of a bar). The millibar is the unit of pressure shown on weather maps. So, a pressure of 970 mbar is below the standard, and pressure which is this low usually means gales. Nowadays, scientists usually measure pressure in units called pascals.

The lines on a weather map join points of equal pressure and are called isobars. They are rather like contour lines on an ordnance survey map. When the lines are close together the ground is steep; when the isobars are close together the pressure gradient is steep and the winds blow strongly.

Measuring temperature

The energy from the Sun very largely determines the temperature on the Earth, and very small shifts in temperature could be having a major effect on the Earth's climate.

Temperature measurement is determined by comparison with well-defined fixed points. There are a number of these to cover the temperature range, for example the triple point of water 0.01°C or the freezing point of pure gold, 1064°C. The standards for these fixed points are held by the NPL and it provides a service to customers who wish to make their own special thermometers and need to calibrate them.

Forecasting weather

It is possible to know what the wind speeds, pressure, temperature and other facts about the atmosphere are over the entire surface of the Earth any time we wish. But all this information would be of little use in weather forecasting, for weather is a three-dimensional business! For forecasting, it is essential also to have data about the air above the surface, preferably to a level of at least 20 km. One of the ways of doing this is by the release of gas-filled balloons fitted with measuring instruments and radio transmitters. This is called a 'radiosonde' system and has been of great benefit in the past and still finds uses for getting precise atmospheric information in very localised regions such as the inside of cloud formations. Specially equipped aircraft are also used to gather information very accurately in situations where weather conditions are

(Below) The British Isles, as seen from a weather satellite.

changing rapidly, for example in the 'eye' of a hurricane. But the most important method of monitoring and measuring atmospheric conditions is by satellites.

The era of meteorological satellites began in the 1960s, opening up new possibilities for monitoring the weather from space. The satellites achieve a regular coverage of the whole globe that would be impossible from surface platforms, balloons and aircraft. One of the advantages of monitoring by satellite is the availability of pictures which reveal cloud systems.

Rain at 2pm can be inconvenient if you don't expect it.

(Above left) View of a severe hurricane from a satellite.

(Above right) Satellite showing cloud formations over southern Europe.

Geostationary satellites were an idea proposed by Arthur C Clarke in a science fiction book published in 1952. It was known that the further from the Earth a satellite orbited then the slower it went. He suggested that there must be a distance where the orbit took 24 hours; the satellite would then remain stationary over one spot. He was right; the distance is 36 000 km above the Earth's equator, and now we have satellite TV using aerials which are aimed at a fixed point in the sky where the satellite always is. The aerial itself does not have to be moved.

From this distance a camera on the satellite can photograph a huge area of the Earth's surface, but it cannot see the polar regions. Five such satellites can cover the whole Earth between 50°N and 50°S. Powerful lenses aimed by remote control take detailed pictures of our weather systems and transmit them to Earth as radio signals, where the data is reassembled into an image just like on a TV set.

Satellites which orbit in a North–South direction fly much lower and provide more detailed pictures. By flying lower they orbit much faster, but they move relative to a point on the Earth's surface and can take pictures of any one position every half hour.

All these measurements are fed into huge computers which assemble and store the global weather patterns and, on the basis of these records, daily weather forecasting is now a much more accurate process. Weather forecasts are generally reliable but unexpected rain at 2pm can be a major inconvenience.

The greenhouse effect

The Earth receives energy from the Sun and loses energy by radiation itself which goes out into space. If it receives more energy than it loses then the temperature will rise, and current research suggests that weather patterns will change and our whole climate will alter. This might give the South Coast a Mediterranean climate or it might put London under 10 metres of sea water due to the polar ice caps melting.

The frequency of radiated energy is determined by the temperature of the radiating body. The hot Sun radiates energy with a higher frequency than the energy radiated by the cooler Earth. The 'greenhouse gases' will allow higher frequency energy to pass through but will not allow lower frequency energy back out. So, the energy from the Sun – being high frequency – passes through the atmosphere, but the low frequency energy radiated by the Earth is trapped. The effect is just like a greenhouse in a garden, where the glass behaves like the pollution in the atmosphere, and so the temperature of the Earth rises as the infra-red energy is trapped.

Carbon dioxide (CO_2) is one of the worst greenhouse gases, and the monitoring of CO_2 production at industrial sites is one of the valuable environmental services pioneered by the NPL.

Measuring pollution

Industrial processes often produce waste products which are harmful to the environment. CO_2 is a greenhouse gas, as we have seen; sulphur dioxide (SO_2) dissolves in the water in the atmosphere to produce sulphuric acid, and this then falls as acid rain. Other pollutants, such as chlorofluorocarbons (CFCs), deplete the ozone (O_3) layer which protects the Earth from the Sun's harmful ultraviolet rays. The NPL has developed a system which can accurately measure how much pollutant there is over a wide area, and it can do this quickly.

Two pulses of laser energy are sent out, one at a wavelength which will be absorbed by the pollutant to be measured and one at a similar wavelength level which will not be absorbed. This acts as a reference. By observing the difference between the scattering of the measuring beam and the second reference beam we can calculate how much of a particular pollutant there is and at what distance – this is called a concentration profile.

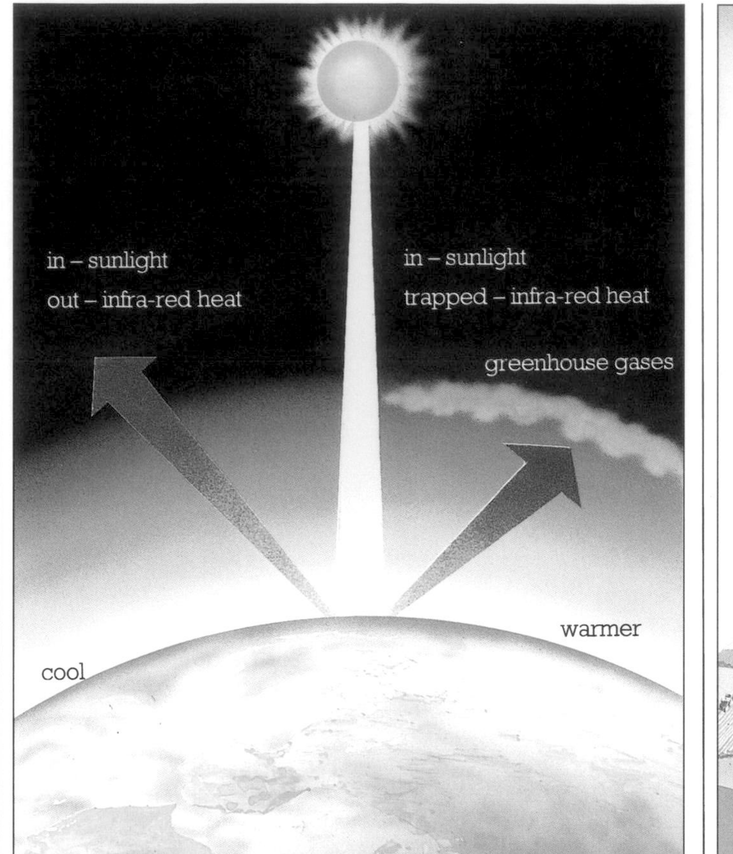

The greenhouse effect.

Bursts of laser light are scattered by different kinds of molecules in different ways. By looking at the way in which the light is scattered we can measure how much of a particular molecule is present in the atmosphere. It is really better to call it laser energy, as very often the wavelength is just outside the visible spectrum.

Advanced laser instruments measuring atmospheric pollution.

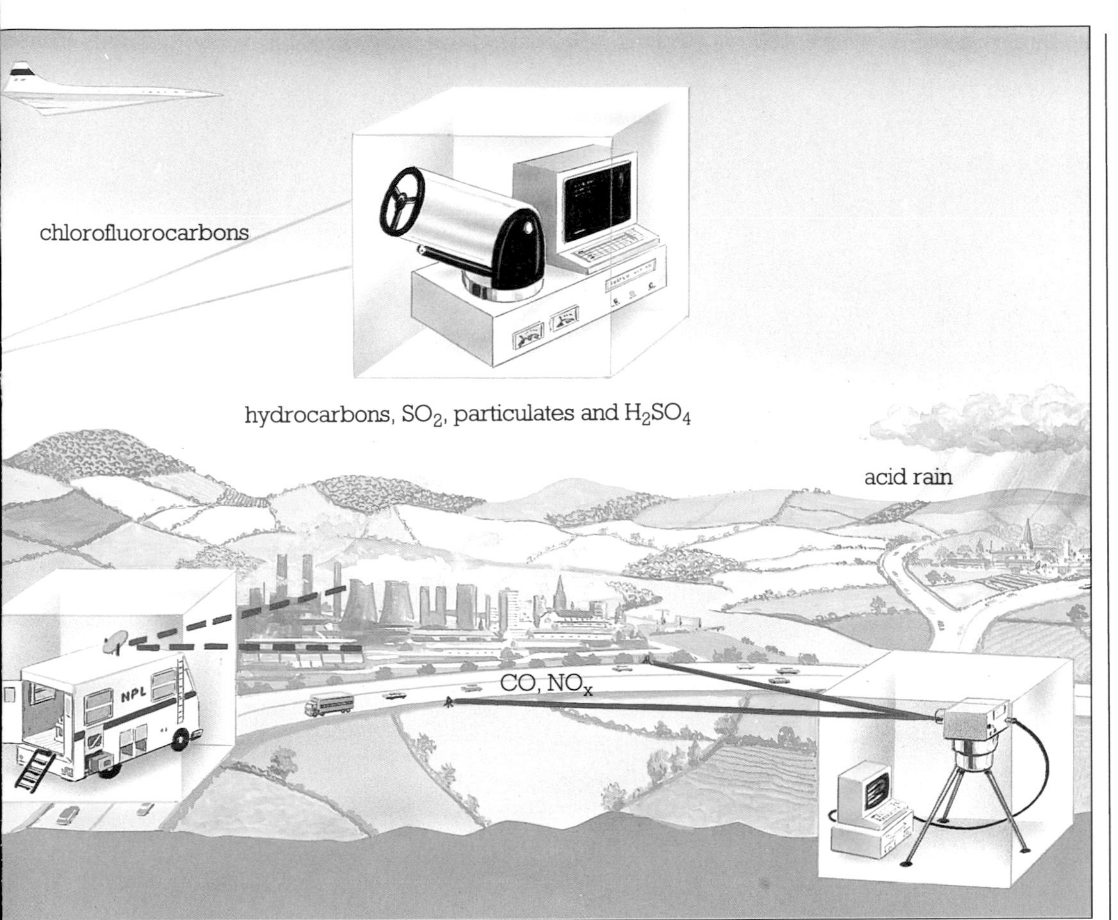

Measuring man's impact on the environment.

The big advantage with laser technology is that measurements can be made at a distance. The NPL has developed an infra-red laser which can be used at distances of up to 3 km. This means that concentration profiles can be measured from safe and accessible locations – there is no need to climb to the top of the chimney to measure what is coming out. It also means that concentration profiles over wide areas can be measured from one location, and mobile laboratories can carry sophisticated equipment. The laser is relatively straightforward (see chapter 3), but the instruments which detect and measure energy scattered over 3 km away are necessarily very sensitive and complex.

The NPL has developed two systems which, between them, measure a very wide range of pollutants which are responsible for acid rain and urban smog. They can also measure the emissions from car engines and industrial plant.

By providing very accurate mixtures of gases in the laboratory as standards for comparison, these systems are proving very valuable in the fight against pollution.

A high-energy infra-red laser system for remote measurements in atmospheric gases at NPL.

Turn it down!

Noise is certainly a nuisance, whether you cannot quite hear the track that is playing on someone else's personal stereo or whether the aircraft flying overhead means that you cannot hear your own. Noise is a pollutant – it spoils the environment for others and leads to stress-induced illness if you are exposed to it for long periods.

Measuring sound as pollution is a service performed by the NPL. It has mobile equipment which is taken to sources of noise – such as the end of a runway – and it records the sound levels, which are then compared with laboratory standards to determine whether the aircraft is breaking the law. Similarly, aircraft engine manufacturers, such as Rolls-Royce, need to know how much noise their engines produce before they can sell them, and extensive noise tests are made with equipment calibrated by the NPL.

As well as keeping the noise down, acoustic measurements are also necessary to help people hear, so the design of recording studios, concert halls and theatres draws heavily on scientific measurements.

Sound is measured by the amount of energy passing through a unit area per second. The units are watts/metre squared. If you stand 1 m away from a low-power (40 W) light-bulb the amount of energy flow will be roughly 3 W m^{-2}. The equivalent amount of sound energy would be extremely painful as the ear is very sensitive. This is why personal stereos do not need a very large power output – also, nearly all the sound goes straight into your ears!

The scale for sound is the decibel (dB) scale . This is a logarithmic scale which means that each time the measured sound increases by ten points on the scale the energy is *ten times* greater. The lowest point on the scale is the quietest sound a normal ear can detect, while the top of the scale, 120 dB, is the threshold of physical pain.

Jet engine thrust measurement using NPL-calibrated load cells.

7: MEASUREMENTS WE CANNOT SEE

Measurement has developed on a human scale, and our units are human size. This is probably because of our need to trade and create wealth. Markets cannot function unless buyers and sellers use information which means the same to both of them and which they can both measure. What if we want to describe something outside the scale of human experience?

How big is the Earth? This is a problem that cannot be directly solved. We could not, until the advent of space travel, see the whole Earth, and a piece of string is just not that long! How far away is the nearest star? At least we can see it, but we cannot reach it! Large measurements have been interesting scientists for thousands of years.

Early steps

How high is that tree? The ancient Greeks had a unit of length based on an average human pace – the problem is that you cannot walk up a tree. They solved the problem with geometry.

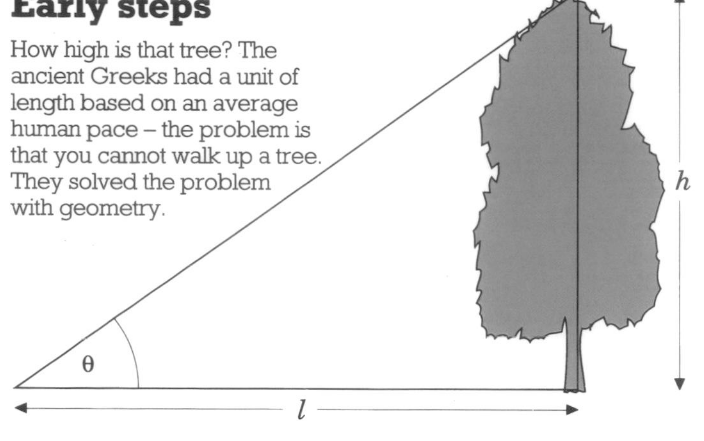

$\tan \theta = \frac{h}{l}$

By drawing a triangle and measuring the lengths of two sides and an angle they found that these measurements were related by the equation

$\frac{h}{l}$ = the tangent of the angle θ (or tan θ).

They stood at a distance of l metres away from the tree and measured the angle θ between the ground and the top of the tree. The Greeks could then calculate the height of the tree. This method of measurement is called triangulation.

ACTIVITY
How can you solve this problem by drawing a triangle and taking measurements from your drawing? There is no need to use tan θ.

Earth, as seen from the moon.

Eratosthenes solved a bigger problem. When he was on holiday at Syrene, near the river Nile in Egypt, Eratosthenes noticed that at midday a stick in the ground cast absolutely no shadow. He noticed that shadows got shorter and longer during the day, every day, except one, when they disappeared. On that day when the stick's shadow disappeared he found that he could see a reflection of the Sun at the bottom of a well. This meant that the Sun must have been directly overhead. He went home to Alexandria and, a year later, noticed that on that same day of the year a stick did cast a shadow. From this he concluded that the Earth was not flat but was, in fact, a sphere. This was quite revolutionary – everybody else was convinced that the Earth was flat!

Eratosthenes knew he was right and decided to measure the circumference. He measured the angle the Sun's rays made with the vertical and found it to be 7°. He then hired a man – presumably one with the standard size of pace – and paid him to pace out the distance from Syrene to Alexandria. He knew that this distance represented seven degrees around the Earth and that there were 360° in a full circle. His man told him how far he had walked – we would call it 800 km – and from that he performed the following sum:

$\frac{360}{7} \times 800 = 41\,000$ km approximately

With only sticks, eyes, feet and brains, Eratosthenes had measured the circumference of the Earth. Of course everybody thought he was mad – they could see that the

Earth was flat! In fact, his measurement was accurate to within a few per cent; an astonishing achievement.

ACTIVITY
Draw the diagram that Eratosthenes drew in order to solve his problem.

(Left) Eratosthenes.

Oh yes it is... Oh no it isn't

In sixteen hundred and ten Galileo abolished heaven.

Another scientist who upset everybody by making measurements on a grand scale was Galileo. He was put under house arrest for saying that the Earth moved round the Sun. At the time it was thought that there were seven crystal spheres which surrounded the Earth. The outside sphere was dark and held the fixed stars. Outside this sphere was heaven and below the earth was hell. The stars were holes in the sphere and starlight was the light of heaven shining through.

Complicated models showed how these spheres moved inside each other in order to account for the movement of heavenly bodies.

At about this time telescopes were invented. These enabled Galileo to make really detailed observations of the stars and planets. He concluded that the Earth was not the centre of the Universe and that the motion of the planets was not like the crystal spheres at all. Instead, the Earth actually moved round the Sun. The Church saw this as a direct challenge to the authority of its teaching, and brought him before the Inquisition. He refused to change his beliefs and was kept under house arrest for the rest of his life. He went on using his telescope but went blind because he used it to observe the Sun.

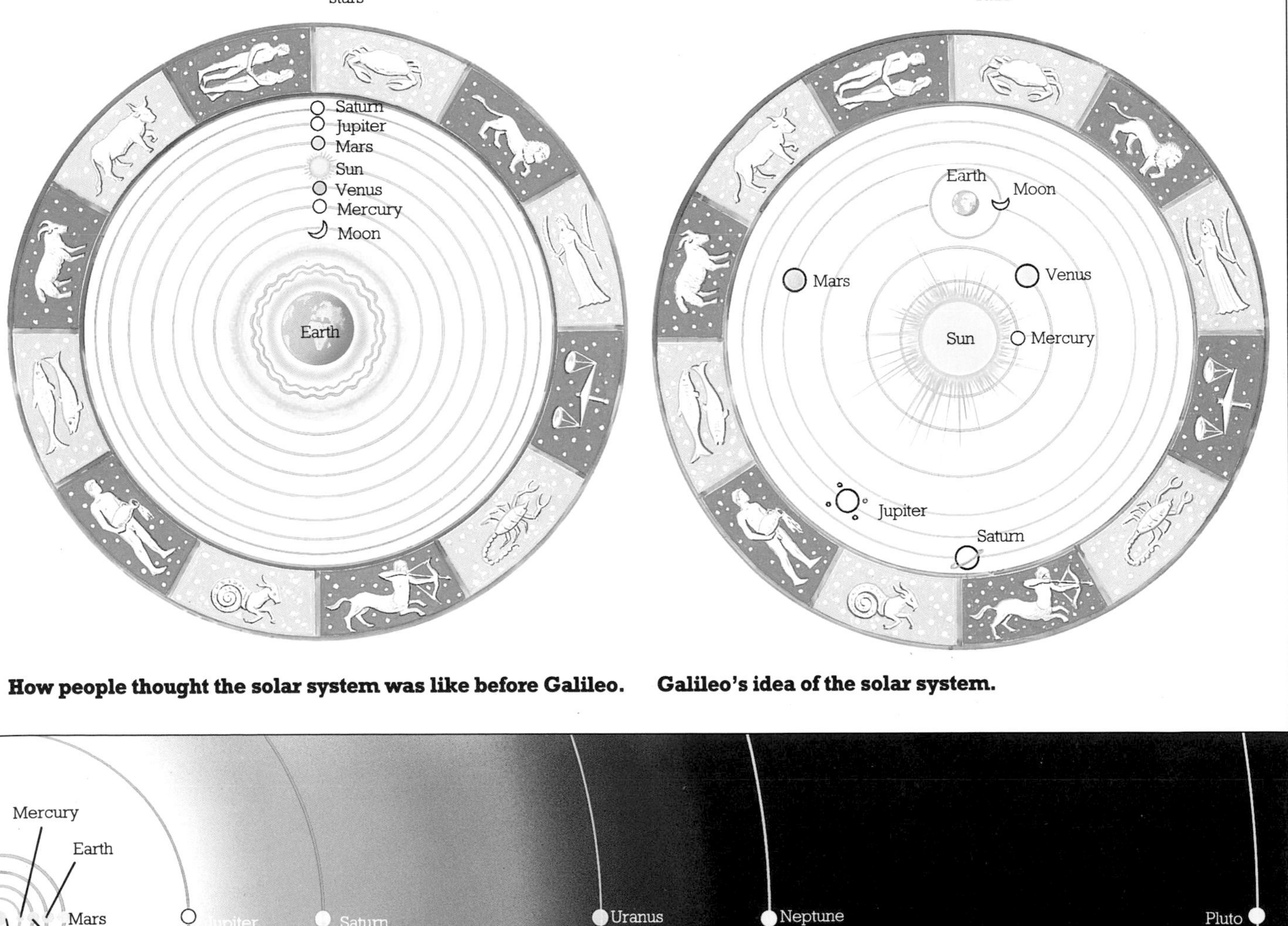

How people thought the solar system was like before Galileo.

Galileo's idea of the solar system.

How we know the solar system today (mean distances only).

Telescopes

The simplest telescope consists of two converging lenses. A converging lens can be used as an ordinary magnifying glass. The one nearest the object is called the objective lens and is usually large and fairly flat. The other lens is the eyepiece and is much fatter. The objective collects light from the object and forms an image; the eyepiece then magnifies that image just like a magnifying glass. This type of telescope is called a refracting telescope. This is the simplest form of astronomical telescope. Very little light reaches the Earth from most objects in the sky, so to get a good view of one the objective lens needs to be as large as possible in order to collect as much light as possible.

A reflecting telescope can be made much larger and can therefore view fainter objects. The light is collected by a large dish-shaped mirror and it is focused to form an image which can be magnified by an eyelens. The mirror can be made so large since its weight can be supported underneath and not just at the edges like a lens, so it is unlikely to break under its own weight. There is one such telescope at Mount Palomar, in California, which measures 5 m in diameter (200 inches).

The problem with optical telescopes is that we have to look through the swirling atmosphere, and this causes the image to jump about (the stars twinkle). Also, it gets cloudy! For this reason telescopes are sited on high mountains so that there is less atmosphere to look through. Tenerife, in the Canary Islands, is a popular site because it has mountains at over 4 000 m and is well away from the pollution caused by cities.

Nineteenth-century model of Sir Isaac Newton's reflecting telescope, made around 1670.

61 inch reflecting telescope of the US Naval Observatory, Washington DC.

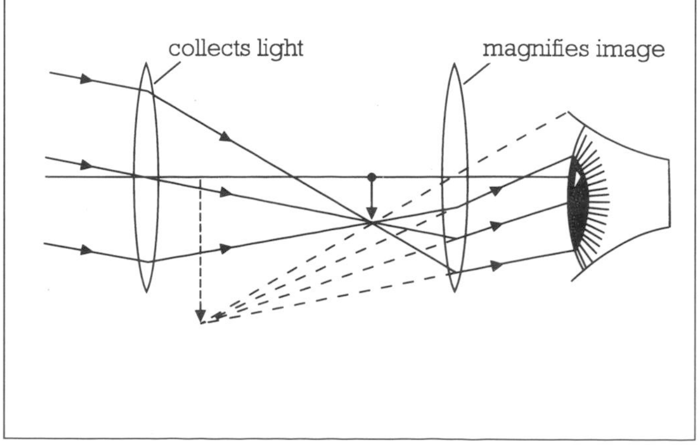

Principle of a refracting telescope.

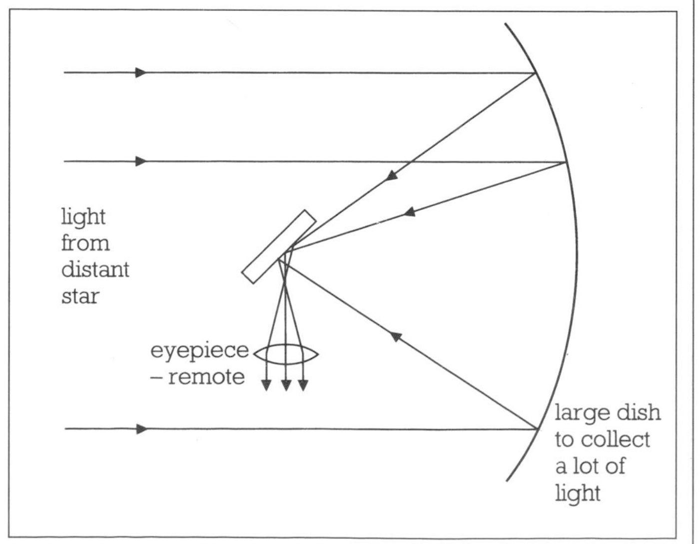

Principle of a reflecting telescope.

The best place of all to view from is space. The American space shuttle has launched the most recent telescope. The Hubble telescope is positioned well above the murky atmosphere, in Earth orbit, from where the pictures are transmitted by radio signal for electronic assembly. It is rather like a huge orbiting TV camera, and should take some superb pictures if early problems are sorted out. Just as our local star – the Sun – emits radiation across the whole range of the electromagnetic spectrum, so do most objects in the sky. Capturing the radio frequency (rf) energy is the job of radio telescopes, and observations made in the rf band show that some objects emit much more rf energy than they do visible light energy. Thus the radio telescope gives us much more information about the Universe – we have, for example, discovered pulsars, which are like rf lighthouses.

Radio waves have a much lower frequency than visible light, so the telescopes need to be very much larger. They are usually large reflecting dishes with the receiving aerial at the focus point. Jodrell Bank is the site for the UK's most famous radio telescope. The biggest single dish is carved out of the mountains in Arecibo, in Mexico. It is 328 m in diameter, but it is the radio equivalent of a small optical telescope. To get better pictures and more accurate measurements scientists have copied Eratosthenes and used geometry to solve their problem.

ACTIVITY
Take two different lenses. Hold the thicker one closer to your eye and move the thinner one at arm's length until you see a really big image through both lenses. You should focus on something at least 20 m away.
REMEMBER: **You must not look at the Sun through a telescope or binoculars. You could seriously damage your eyes!**

View of some of the dish antennae which make up the Very Large Array (VLA) radio telescope near Socorro, New Mexico.

Measuring the stars

How far away is our nearest neighbour? In order to measure interstellar distances we use other units to keep the numbers simpler. For small distances we use the Astronomical Unit (AU), which is the mean distance from the centre of the Earth to the centre of the Sun. $1AU = 1.49 \times 10^{11}$ m. For intergalactic distances we use the light year.

The metre is the distance travelled by light in a vacuum in

$$\frac{1}{299\,792\,458}$$

of a second. The light year is the distance travelled by light in one whole year! Notice it is a measure of distance not time.

On this scale our nearest neighbour in our own galaxy, Alpha Centauri, is just over 4 light years away. Our nearest neighbouring galaxy is thousands of light years away. But how do we measure it?

As we have seen (page 40) the Greeks used an angle and a length to measure the height of a tree. Surveyors on land and astronomers in the sky use two angles and a length in a process of triangulation – see the illustration on the right.

(Top) Optical photograph of the Large Magellanic Cloud (LMC), a small, irregular galaxy seen only from the southern hemisphere.

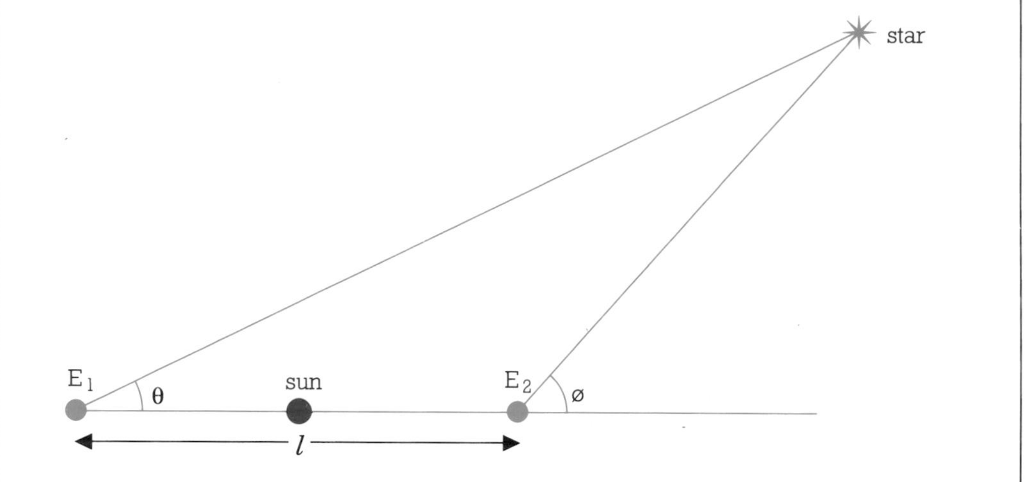

(Above) Triangulation. If the length of the baseline, l, is known and the two angles are known, we can construct a triangle and calculate the length of the sides.

Light travels at 3×10^8 m s^{-1}

So, in one year $= \frac{365 \text{ days}}{\text{year}} \times \frac{24 \text{ hours}}{\text{day}} \times \frac{60 \text{ min}}{\text{hour}} \times \frac{60}{\text{seconds}}$

$= 31\,536\,000$ seconds

1 light year $= 3 \times 10^8$ m s$^{-1} \times 31\,536\,000$ s
$= 9\,460\,800\,000\,000\,000$ m
$= 9.46 \times 10^{15}$

1 light minute $= 3 \times 10^8$ m s$^{-1} \times 60$ s
$= 18\,000\,000\,000$ m
$= 1.8 \times 10^{10}$ m

We can therefore describe long distances in terms of the speed of light.

For example, the centre of the Sun is 1.49×10^{11} m away from the centre of the Earth.

$$1.49 \times 10^{11} \text{ m} = \frac{1.49 \times 10^{11}}{1.8 \times 10^{10}} = 8.28 \text{ light minutes}$$

This means that the sunlight we see every day takes just over 8 minutes to reach us.

By measuring these angles using telescopes we can measure huge distances providing the baseline is long enough to make the angles large enough to measure. If one observation is made on 1 January and the next one on 1 July, then the baseline will be equal to the diameter of the Earth's orbit around the Sun which is 3×10^{11} m. This enables us to measure these huge distances across the empty wastes of space, but how do we observe what is out there?

Radio telescopes use the principle of interference to measure distance, just like lasers. If several observations are made at the same time by different telescopes, their signals can be recorded and compared later. This gives the same effect as having a single dish several km wide. Images of a distant galaxy made in this way showed that it consists of a gigantic gas cloud with a hole in it. The hole is of great interest – it should not be there! But to find it at all was a triumph – one scientist compared it to seeing the hole in a polo mint at a distance of 3 km.

Distance and time

Galactic distances can now be measured with great accuracy. When we look at distant galaxies, the light has taken tens of millions of years to arrive. This means that the light left that galaxy in the distant past, before the Earth was formed. Observing distant galaxies is literally looking back in time.

Too small to measure

At much the same time as the telescope was invented, so was the microscope. This enables us to measure structures which are too small to be seen. Again, the simplest type has just two lenses. Magnifications of over 2000 times are readily achieved using carefully manufactured lenses. The NPL does much research into optics and develops the relevant national standards for optics so that it can provide calibration and consultancy services so that manufacturers can produce accurate equipment. Your glasses or contact lenses were probably manufactured by equipment calibrated against NPL standards. Mirrors and lenses need to be produced to highly accurate standards of curvature. If these standards are not maintained, accurate measurements are just not possible and even large telescopes will produce fuzzy images.

Optical microscopes can examine structures as small as 1/1000th of a millimetre (1 μm). The limiting factor is the wavelength of light. Light has a wavelength of about 0.5 μm and this is as small as we can see.

Just as astronomy has been improved by 'looking' outside the visible spectrum, so has microscopy. In order to make even smaller measurements we use an electron microscope. Fast-moving electrons behave just like particles of light in that they have a wavelength, they can be focused using 'lenses' and even produce interference patterns just like light waves. The wavelength of these electrons is 1000 times shorter than that of visible light, so we can investigate structures as small as 1 thousandth of a micrometre, or 10^{-6} m or 1 nanometre. The 'lenses' are no longer made of glass but are electromagnetic coils, and since we cannot see at this wavelength the microscopes need special photographic film or something like a TV screen in order to detect the image. But electron microscopes enable scientists to investigate individual molecules.

(Top Right) In the scanning electron microscope (SEM).

(Centre Right) False-colour scanning EM of a pollen grain from a hollyhock.

(Bottom Right) False-colour scanning EM showing human red blood cells.

(Below) False-colour scanning EM of bacteria (yellow) on the head of a pin.

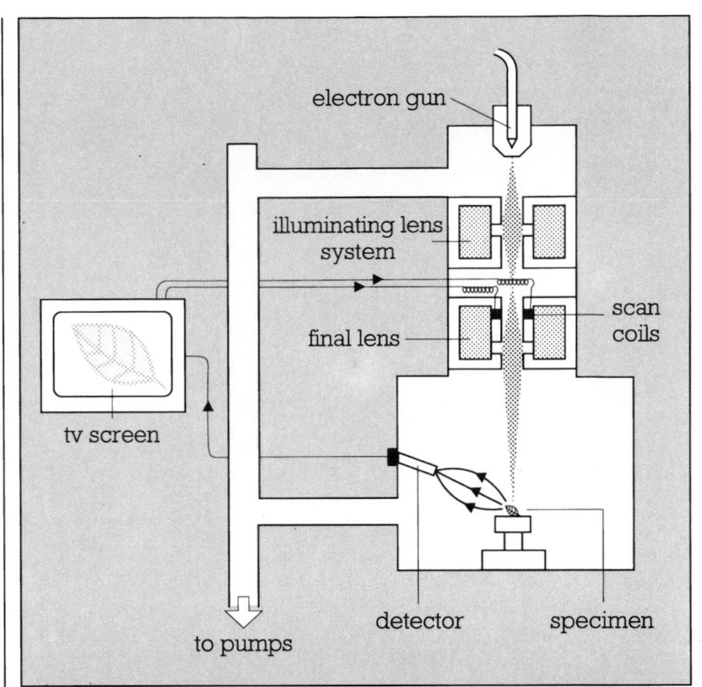

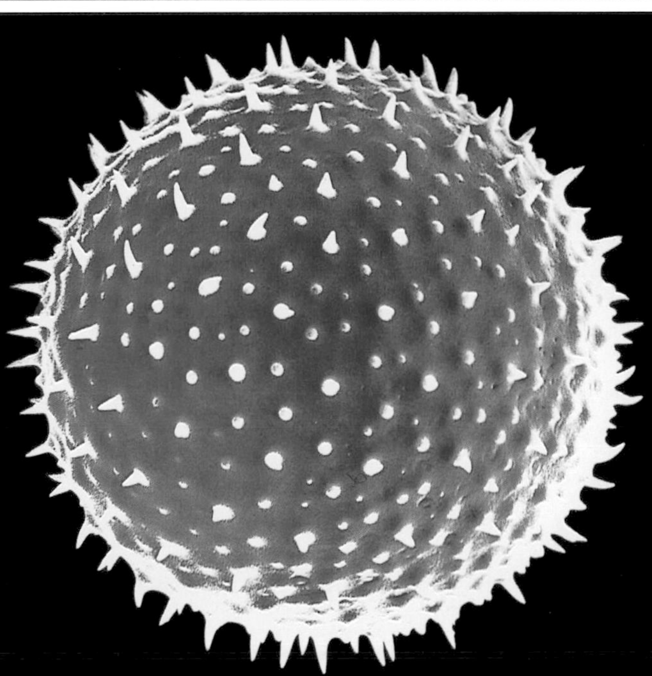

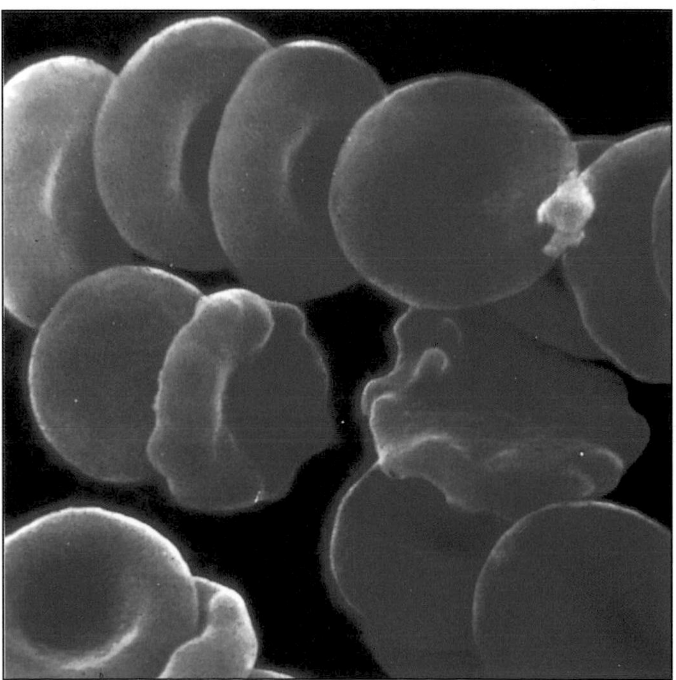

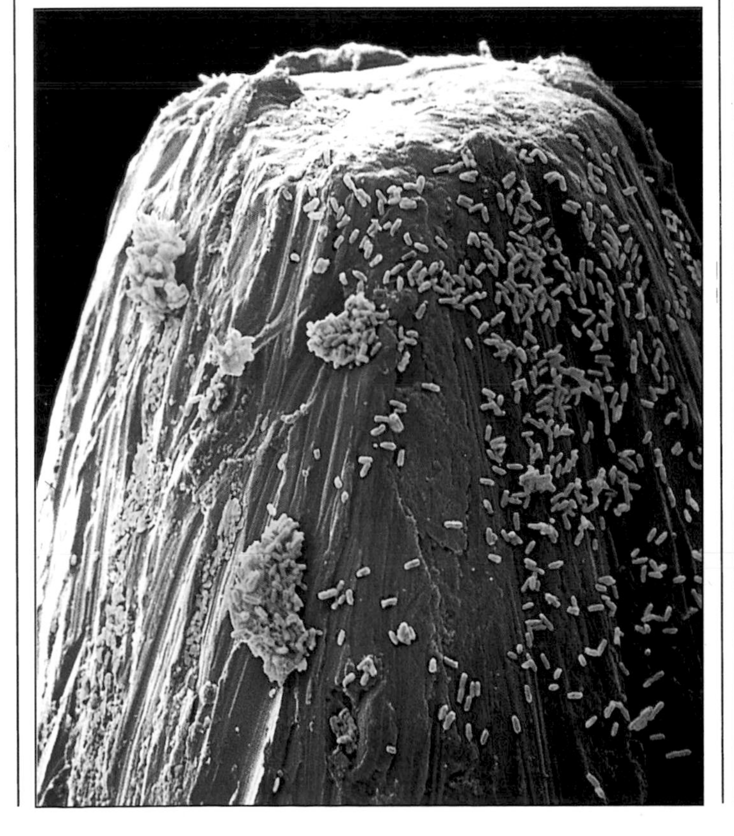

8: THE ROLE OF THE NPL

The National Physical Laboratory (NPL), an Agency of the Department of Trade and Industry, is the UK's **national standards laboratory**. Reliable measurement of all physical quantities – for example of length, mass, force, pressure, temperature, time and voltage – is very important to both industry and government. It plays an essential role in manufacture, commerce, health, safety and other areas. To meet the needs of these sectors, the Laboratory establishes and maintains a consistent **National Measurement System** based on national measurement standards and coordinated with those of other countries with which we trade. The programmes of research and the international measurement comparisons necessary to support these functions are also undertaken. The NPL provides essential calibration, laboratory accreditation and consultancy services for a very wide range of users.

The Laboratory also has another important function: to carry out standards research in certain key scientific and technological areas chosen for their national importance. Current work includes research on engineering materials and information technology (IT). A wide range of services in all these areas is available to customers.

The scientific work of the Laboratory is undertaken in six Divisions:

Mechanical and Optical Metrology – engineering metrology*, covering dimensional, mechanical and optical measurement;

Materials Metrology – engineering materials, surface properties and corrosion;

Quantum Metrology – thermal metrology, optical radiation standards, atmospheric measurements, innovative metrology and fundamental constants;

Electrical Science – electrical metrology from DC to the highest frequencies;

Radiation Science and Acoustics – metrology for ionising radiations, acoustics, medical and industrial ultrasound;

Information Technology and Computing – standards for IT, human-machine interaction and numerical software.

The Laboratory is also the base for the **National Measurement Accreditation Service (NAMAS)** which provides accreditation* for calibration and testing laboratories.

* metrology = the scientific study of weights and measures.

* accreditation = official recognition.

Information concerning the work of the NPL is available from:
Information Services
National Physical Laboratory
Teddington
Middlesex

Tel: 081 977 3222

The **National Measurement System** enables an individual or organisation to have the means to carry out competently the measurement of any physical quantity to any desired, but reasonable, degree of accuracy. The diagram illustrates the main links of the system from NPL to the final user in industry, trade and commerce or to the consumer.

NPL is the focus of the **National Measurement System** and maintains the national standards for virtually all the important physical and engineering quantities. The National Engineering

Direct Links

National Weights & Measures Laboratory – legal metrology

Laboratory of the Government Chemist – chemical measurement

Other national laboratories

Department of Health – secondary laboratories in hospitals

National Measurement Accreditation Service – accredited laboratories

The National Measurement System

Laboratory (NEL) is responsible, however, for the national standards for flow measurement, and a few other centres for some quantities of lesser general importance.

NAMAS. The National Measurement Accreditation Service is a service of NPL through which calibration and testing laboratories are accredited as competent to undertake specific types of calibration and testing.

Accredited laboratories. These laboratories, mainly located within private industry, are recognised as offering calibration and testing services that meet the very high standards demanded for accreditation by NAMAS.

Direct links. NPL maintains strong direct links to industry in order to meet calibration requirements outside the scope of accredited laboratories, to assist in anticipating the future requirements for national standards and to undertake technology transfer activities in key technological areas.

EUROMET. NPL maintains links with other national standards laboratories to ensure a consistent measurement system throughout the world. Within Europe, a collaborative activity called EUROMET has been established to further advance international collaboration in the development and dissemination of measurement standards.

National Weights and Measures Laboratory (NWML). This laboratory, an Agency of the Department of Trade and Industry, is responsible for the calibration of the standards used by local trading standards officers to check the accuracy of equipment used in shops, garages, public houses, etc. NWML maintains secondary standards traceable to NPL.

Laboratory of the Government Chemist (LGC). This laboratory, an Agency of the Department of Trade and Industry, is the focus for chemical measurement within the National Measurement System.

Department of Health secondary laboratories in hospitals. The dissemination of radiation dosimetry standards for therapeutic purposes to hospitals is done through a series of regional centres in Department of Health hospitals that, in turn, maintain standards that are traceable to NPL.

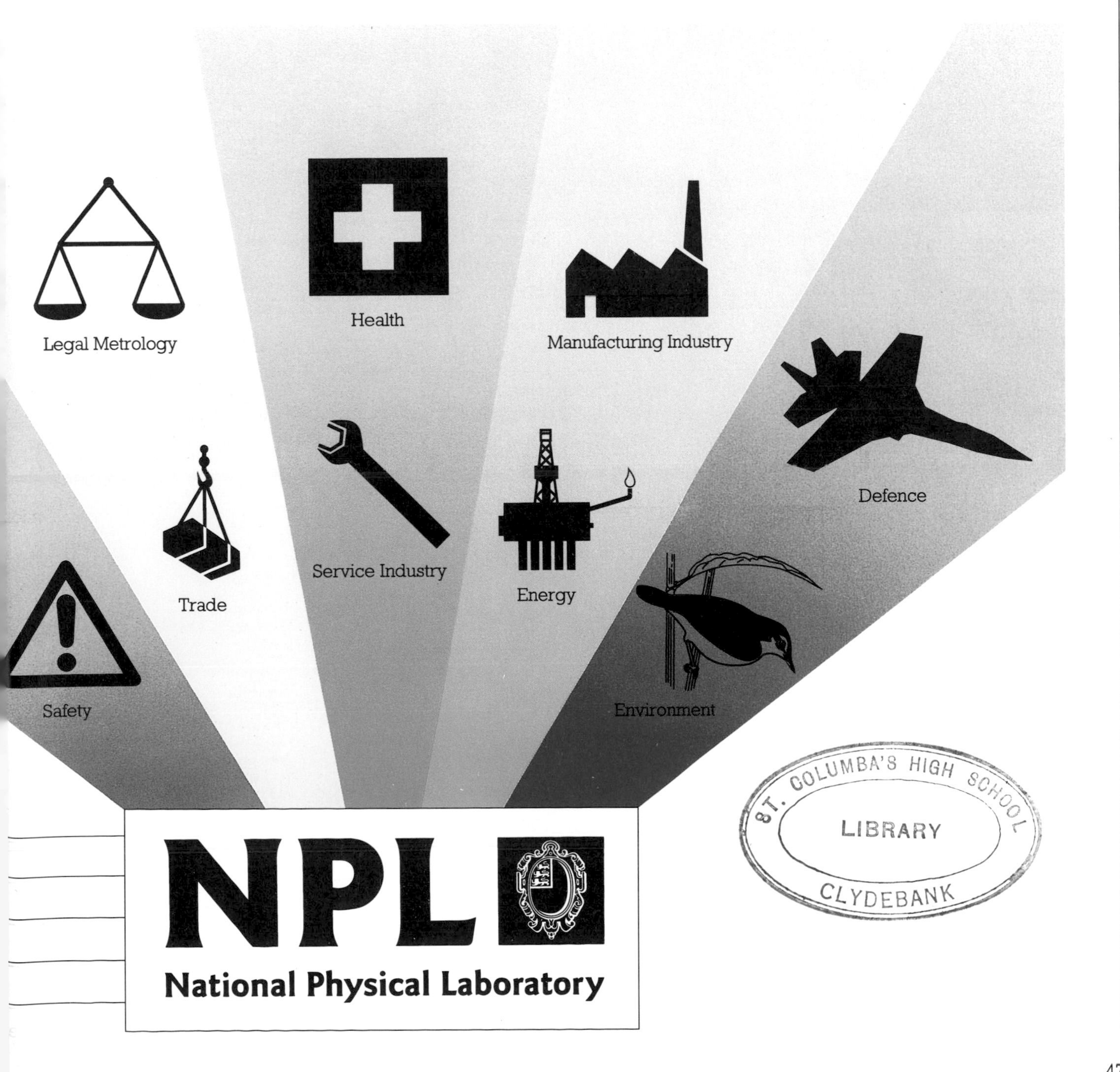

Index